THE

Maria Thun

BIODYNAMIC
CALENDAR
2024

CREATED BY
MARIA AND MATTHIAS THUN

Floris
Books

Floris Books is proud to be part of the international biodynamics movement. We aim to support biodynamic farmers, small-holders, wine-makers and gardeners by publishing informative and inspiring books, calendars and apps.

Compiled by Titia and Friedrich Thun
Translated by Bernard Jarman
Additional astronomical material
by Wolfgang Held and Christian Maclean

Published in German as *Aussaattage*
English edition published by Floris Books

British Library CIP Data available
ISBN 978-178250-870-0
ISSN: 2052-5761
Printed in Poland through Hussar

Printed on recycled paper made from 100% post-consumer waste.

Uses plant-based inks which reduce chemical emissions and makes this book easier to recycle.

RECYCLED
Made from recycled material
FSC
www.fsc.org FSC® C167221

Contents

Preface

Despite it being two years since the centenary of her birth, in this edition we would like to focus on Maria Thun. Among her greatest achievements are her preparations, which we will describe again in detail. We constantly receive questions about the use of the barrel (cow pat) preparation and above all about the tree bark preparations. We hope to discuss these in more detail in a future book about the preparations. However, as we cannot yet say when this book will be published, we are addressing this topic now. We will describe the origins and history of both preparations as well as giving precise instruction on making them and their application.

As an introduction to these two articles, we will also briefly retell her biography. It is not the first time that her story has been told in this calendar: it was done over ten years ago for the fiftieth anniversary of the (German) calendar. However, with the passage of time, we consider it appropriate to look at Maria Thun and her work again.

Titia and Friedrich Thun

What are the basic principles of the calendar?

The information in this guide is based on over sixty years of research by Maria Thun, who lived in central Germany and for over fifty years produced this annual calendar. After her death in 2012 her son Matthias continued the work, and it is now produced by her grandchildren, Titia and Friedrich.

The principle that underlies this guide is that the Moon has a significant influence on the Earth. Not only does it control the tides, but it influences all living organisms, including the way plants grow.

From our perspective on Earth, the Sun passes through twelve star constellations every year – the signs of the zodiac, from Aries to Pisces. The Moon also passes through these constellations, but because the Moon circles the Earth about once a month, it passes through all twelve constellations in that time.

Each constellation is associated with one of the four classical elements – earth, water, air or fire. And each of these elements affects a different part of a plant:

- the earth element affects the roots
- the water element affects the leaves
- the air element affects the flowers
- and the fire element affects the fruit and seed

It is easy to understand why: the roots are down in the earth, the leaves are full of water, the flowers' perfume is carried by the air, and fire (or warmth) is essential for fruit to ripen.

Through the course of many agricultural trials over several decades, Maria Thun showed that plants thrived, yields were increased, and harvested produce lasted longer if plants were tended at specific times, according to the part of the plant that the grower wanted to enhance. For example, carrots thrived if they were tended during root times, and apples thrived if they were tended during fruit times. This calendar gives you all the information you need to tend your plants at the best possible times, for the best possible outcomes.

The details of this calendar take into account all aspects of lunar and solar cycles, star constellations and the movement of planets. It is used every year by people all over the world to decide when to sow, plant and harvest fruit (including grapes for making biodynamic wine), vegetables, flowers and crops, as well as by beekeepers and people who make butter and cheese, since all of these are influenced by the movement of the Moon.

How do I use the calendar?

Different parts of a plant are cultivated for food or other uses. Plants can therefore be divided into four groups:

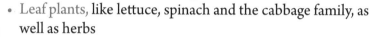
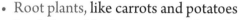
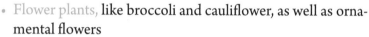
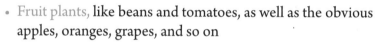

- Root plants, like carrots and potatoes
- Leaf plants, like lettuce, spinach and the cabbage family, as well as herbs
- Flower plants, like broccoli and cauliflower, as well as ornamental flowers
- Fruit plants, like beans and tomatoes, as well as the obvious apples, oranges, grapes, and so on

There is a full list of types of plants on p. 66 so you can be confident about which type of plant you're growing.

The growth of all garden and farm plants and crops is enhanced when the plants are sown, transplanted, hoed, weeded, cut back and even harvested when the Moon is in a constellation that matches the plant type.

The twelve constellations are grouped into four different types, which correspond to the four types of time in this guide:

- Virgo (♍), Capricorn (♑), Taurus (♉)   Root
- Libra (♎), Aquarius (♒), Gemini (♊)   Flower
- Scorpio (♏), Pisces (♓), Cancer (♋)   Leaf
- Sagittarius (♐), Aries (♈), Leo (♌)   Fruit/seed

What's shown in the calendar?

The dates are listed down the left-hand column

The hours are listed along the top, from 0 (midnight) to 12 (noon) and on to 24 (midnight again)

Transplanting Time (see p. 11)

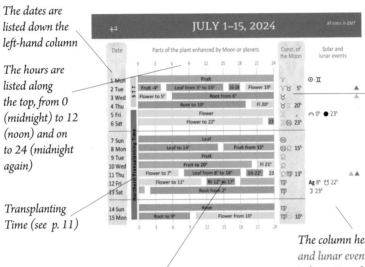

The column headed *Const. of the Moon* shows which star constellation the Moon is passing through on that day

The horizontal coloured bars show the hours that are optimal for working on which type of plants. There are four types of time: *Root (brown bar), Flower (yellow bar), Leaf (green bar)* and *Fruit (red bar).* **There are also grey bars which are unfavourable times for working on any crop. (To find out why, skip ahead to 'Why are other astronomical events important' p. 12.)**

The column headed *Solar and lunar events* shows other information about the Moon, Sun and sometimes other astronomical events. (You'll find more about that in 'I'd like to understand the astronomy in more detail' p. 10.)

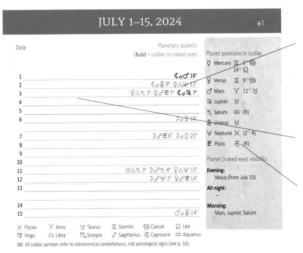

Planetary aspects and other astronomical information (see 'Why are other astronomical events important' p.12) are indicated on the right

There is space for your own notes here

The final (tinted) column shows which constellation the planets are in, and purely for those interested in astronomy, the naked-eye visibility of the planets (see 'Planets' p. 14)

Times and symbols

What time zone is the calendar in?

The times shown in this calendar are GMT. In the UK and Ireland remember to add an hour to all the times during British Summer Time.

If you are not in the UK, you'll need to add or subtract from the times in the charts according to your location (see page 17 'Converting to local times'). If you download the companion Biodynamic Gardening Calendar app, which uses data from this calendar and allows you to look up planting information while you're on the go, the app adjusts the times automatically to your location, but does not give as much detail as the printed calendar. (Details of the app are on the inside back cover).

Note that Fruit, Flower, Root and Leaf times normally don't last for precisely one day. The Moon moves in and out of different constellations at different times, so a Flower time might start at 11 am on a Monday and finish at 5 pm on a Wednesday. Use the coloured bars to pinpoint whether conditions are favourable at a particular time on a particular day.

Do I need to understand all the symbols?

You do not need to understand all the astronomical background to grow better vegetables! If it is too daunting, just ignore it and follow the practical hints for the type of plant you are growing at the times shown by the horizontal coloured bars.

Why does the calendar recommend certain activities in the middle of the night?

Don't worry, no midnight planting is required! The calendar works for gardeners and farmers around the world, and one person's midnight is another person's morning or early evening. Just choose the times that work best for you. There are usually plenty of options for tending each type of plant.

Why does the calendar recommend that I harvest and store leaf plants during a Fruit and Flower times?

It may seem counter-intuitive, but it has been shown that Fruit and Flower times are best for harvesting and storing leaf plants such as lettuce, spinach and herbs.

I'd like to understand the astronomy in more detail
Star signs and constellations

The **zodiac** is a group of twelve constellations of stars, which the Sun, Moon and all the planets pass through on their circuits as seen from the Earth. We know them as the zodiac – Scorpio, Cancer, Aries, etc. – but in the context of this guide, these names are used to indicate the visible star *constellations* rather than the astrological *signs* used in horoscopes. (For those who are into astronomy and astrology, the difference is that they are out of sync, as shown in the diagram below.)

The Moon takes about 27½ days to orbit the Earth, passing through all twelve constellations in that time. This rhythm is called the *sidereal month.*

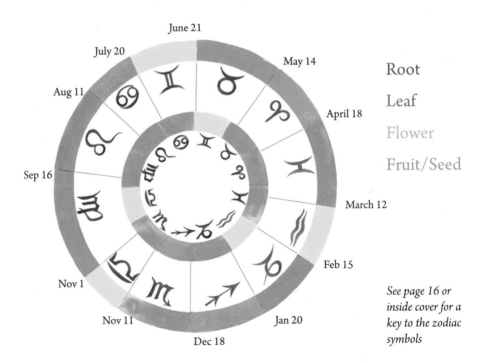

*The outer circle shows the varying sizes of the visible **constellations** of the zodiac. The dates on this outer circle are the approximate dates on which the Sun enters the constellation (from year to year the actual date can change by one day because of leap years). The inner circle shows the divisions into equal sections of 30° corresponding to the **signs** used in astrology.*

Transplanting Time and ascending or descending Moon

From midwinter through to midsummer the Sun rises earlier and sets later each day, and its path across the sky ascends higher and higher. From midsummer until midwinter this is reversed: the days get shorter and the midday Sun shines from an ever-lower point in the sky. This annual ascending and descending of the Sun creates our seasons. In the northern hemisphere the winter solstice occurs in December when the Sun is in the constellation of Sagittarius, and the summer solstice occurs in June when the Sun is in Gemini. At any point from Sagittarius to Gemini, the Sun is ascending, while from Gemini to Sagittarius, it is descending. In the southern hemisphere, this is reversed.

The Moon (and all the planets) follow approximately the same path as the Sun around the zodiac but instead of taking a year, the Moon takes only about 27½ days to complete one cycle. This means that the Moon will ascend for about 14 days, and then descend for about 14 days.

When the Moon is *ascending,* plant sap rises more strongly. The upper part of the plant fills with sap and vitality. This is therefore a good time for cutting scions (young shoots for grafting). Fruit harvested during this period remains fresh for longer when stored.

When the Moon is *descending,* plants take root more readily and connect well with their new location. This period is referred to as the **Transplanting Time**, even though the period is actually optimal for a range of growing activities. Transplanting is when plants are moved from one location to another, for example when young plants are moved from the seedbed into their final growing position, but also when the gardener wishes to strengthen the root development of young fruit trees, shrubs or pot plants by frequently re-potting them. Note that sowing is the moment when a seed is put into the soil, and this can be done during

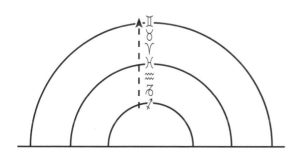

The northern hemisphere ascending Moon, showing the Moon's arc across the sky getting higher and higher for about 14 days, with the Moon moving from Sagittarius to Gemini

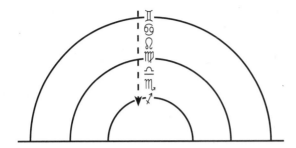

*The northern hemisphere descending Moon (**Transplanting Time**), showing the Moon's arc across the sky getting lower and lower for about 14 days, with the Moon moving from Gemini to Sagittarius*

either the ascending or descending period. We use the term 'transplanting' rather than just 'planting' to avoid confusion with sowing.

Additionally, because sap movement is slower during the descending Moon, it is a good time for trimming hedges, pruning trees and felling timber as well as applying compost to meadows, pastures and orchards.

You will sometimes see a reference to **Northern Transplanting Times** and Southern Transplanting Times. These are just a quick way to refer to the period of the descending Moon in either hemisphere.

In the 'Solar and lunar events' panel the date and time of highest Moon (⌢) is shown, after which the Moon descends, likewise the lowest Moon (⌣) after which the Moon ascends. For the southern hemisphere these are the opposite way round: what is shown as highest Moon is the lowest Moon there.

One final note on the ascending and descending Moon: it is important to distinguish the journey of the Moon through the zodiac (sidereal rhythm) from the phases (waxing and waning); in any given constellation there may be a waxing or waning Moon.

Why are other astronomical events important?

There are many astronomical events in our skies, which also have an effect on the Earth, and this section gives more details about them and their effects.

They are important because some of them have an unfavourable effect on plant growth for some hours, and you shouldn't do any work in the garden during these times. These so-called *unfavourable times* are shown in the calendar as grey horizontal bars.

If you are not interested in astronomy, you can simply skip this section, but avoid doing anything in the garden during unfavourable times.

More Moon rhythms

The phases

The calendar pages show the phases of the Moon under 'Solar and lunar events'.

- ● New Moon
- ☽ Waxing half Moon (first quarter)
- ○ Full Moon
- ☾ Waning half Moon (last quarter)

This rhythm also takes about one month. Called the *synodic month,* it is a little longer – about 29½ days – than the sidereal rhythm, which relates to the movement through the constellations of the zodiac. The synodic month does not have much effect on plant growth, and we take no account of it in this calendar; the phases are merely shown for those people who want to have a complete picture of the Moon's rhythms.

The Moon's nodes

The Moon's path through the zodiac is not exactly the same as the Sun's path (which is called the ecliptic). Seen from the Earth, the Moon's path is inclined by about 5° to the ecliptic. Twice a month, the Moon crosses the ecliptic, the Sun's path. These crossing points are called nodes. One crosses from below the ecliptic to above it and this is called the ascending node (shown as ☊ in the calendar under 'Solar and lunar events'). About two weeks later, it crosses from above to below; this is the descending node (shown as ☋). The times around the nodes are shown as unfavourable times (grey bars in the calendar). Both ascending and descending nodes have a negative effect on plant growth.

Eclipses

If a New Moon occurs at a node there is a solar eclipse, as the Moon is directly in front of the Sun. If a Full Moon occurs at a node there is a lunar eclipse, where the Earth's shadow falls on the Moon. Even if the eclipse is not visible from where you are, it has an unfavourable effect on plant growth and is shown as an unfavourable time in the calendar (grey bars).

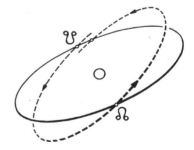

The Sun's path (solid line) and the Moon's path (dashed line) seen from the Earth (centre). The angle is exaggerated for clarity. The descending node (crossing point) is behind, and ascending node in front. (Note that the following node will not be in the same position: the nodes move.)

Apogee and perigee

The Moon travels on an almost circular ellipse around the Earth. This means that sometimes the Moon is a little closer to the Earth, and sometimes a little further away. The point at which the Moon is closest to the Earth is called perigee (shown as **Pg** under 'Solar and lunar events'). Conversely, the point at which the Moon is furthest from the Earth is called apogee (shown as **Ag**).

Perigee (**Pg**) is an unfavourable time (grey bars) for gardening work.

However, around apogee (**Ag**) the Moon stimulates flowering and fruiting. The calendar bars take account of this effect, which can mean that they diverge from the underlying Moon/constellation effect.

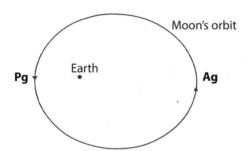

The elliptical orbit of the Moon around the Earth (exaggerated), showing closest (Perigee) and furthest (Apogee) positions

The Sun and the zodiac

The Sun's movement through the zodiac takes a year and determines the seasons on Earth. The constellation through which the Sun is passing is always shown on the first entry of a calendar page, and if it changes during the month that is shown on the appropriate day. Remember that the calendar shows the visible astronomical constellations, and not the astrological signs, so the dates are out of sync! (See p. 10.)

Some activities depend on which constellation the Sun is in (for instance, making biodynamic preparations).

Planets

The planets, too, have an effect on plant growth. The far-right panel on the calendar pages shows which constellation each planet is passing. The planets mostly move in direct motion – that is, in the same direction as the Sun and Moon – but unlike the Moon, for some time they move in the opposite direction, which is called retrograde motion. (Retrograde motion can strengthen the effect of the planet.) This time is shown as R, with the date indicating when the retrograde motion begins. When the planet begins to move in direct motion again, it is shown as D.

The visibility of the planets to the naked eye is shown below this panel. This is purely an aid to personal observation and has no effect at all on farming or gardening. Note that the furthest planets, Neptune, Uranus and Pluto, cannot be seen with the naked eye.

Aspects

Aspects are particular angular relationships of planets, the Sun and the Moon (collectively called *celestial bodies*), as seen from the Earth. The main ones are *conjunctions*, which is when two celestial bodies pass each other; *oppositions*, which is when they are opposite each other; and *trines*, which is when they are 120° apart.

     σ conjunction   ° opposition   ▵ (or ▲) trine

For those interested in observing the planets, the aspects visible to the naked eye are shown in bold type.

Conjunctions

Conjunctions (shown as σ) occur when two planets stand behind one another in space. Usually only the planet closest to the Earth has any influence on plant growth. If this influence is stronger than that of the Moon, cosmic disturbances can occur that irritate the plants and cause problems with growth.

This negative effect is increased if the Moon or Sun stand directly in front of a planet – called an *occultation* (•). In the case of Sun and Moon, this is called an eclipse. Sowing at these times will harm future growth and damage a plant's ability to reproduce. These times are marked as an unfavourable time (grey bar).

Oppositions

An opposition (shown as °) occurs if two celestial bodies are opposite one another – 180° apart. You cannot see both planets during an opposition because one will be above the horizon, the other below. Their rays fall on to the Earth and positively stimulate the seeds sown at that moment. In trials, Maria Thun found that seedlings transplanted at times of opposition resulted in a slightly higher yield. While the opposition is shown under the planetary aspects, it is not otherwise noted on the calendar pages.

Trines

Trines (shown as △) occur when planets are 120° from one another. The two planets are usually both standing in the same type of constellation – Aries and Leo for example are both Fruit (fire or warmth) constellations. Generally, the positive effect of the trine overrules the underlying lunar constellation. There may therefore be a Fruit time shown in the calendar despite the Moon being in a Leaf (or other) constellation. To show that this is deliberate, there is a coloured ▲ under 'Solar and lunar events'.

Sometimes when two planets are in a trine, they are in different types of constellations. The trine is shown as △ under planetary aspects on the right-hand page, but these trines have no effect on plant growth and are not shown as coloured ▲ under 'Solar and lunar events' on the left page.

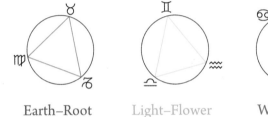

Earth–Root   Light–Flower   Water–Leaf   Warmth–Fruit/ Seed

Types of trine and their constellations

Astronomical symbols

Constellations		Planets		Aspects	
♓	Pisces	☉	Sun	☊	Ascending node
♈	Aries	☽	Moon (first qtr)	☋	Descending node
♉	Taurus	☾	Moon (last qtr)	⌒	Highest Moon
♊	Gemini	☿	Mercury	⌣	Lowest Moon
♋	Cancer	♀	Venus	**Pg**	Perigee
♌	Leo	♂	Mars	**Ag**	Apogee
♍	Virgo	♃	Jupiter	☍	Opposition
♎	Libra	♄	Saturn	☌	Conjunction
♏	Scorpio	♅	Uranus	☄	Eclipse/occultation
♐	Sagittarius	♆	Neptune	☄͘	Lunar eclipse
♑	Capricorn	♇	Pluto	△	Trine (or ▲)
♒	Aquarius	○	Full Moon	D	Direct motion
		●	New Moon	R	Retrograde motion

Converting to local time

Times given are Greenwich Mean Time (GMT), using the 24-hour clock with ^{h} after the time. Thus 15^h is 3 pm. **No account is taken of daylight saving (summer) time (DST).** Note 0^h is midnight at the beginning of a date, and 24^h is midnight at the end of the date.

Add (+) or subtract (–) times as below. For countries not listed check local time against GMT.

Europe

Britain, Ireland, Portugal: GMT (DST March 31 to Oct 26, $+1^h$)
Iceland: GMT (no DST)
Central Europe: $+1^h$ (DST March 31 to Oct 26, $+2^h$)
Eastern Europe (Finland etc.): $+2^h$ (DST March 31 to Oct 26, $+3^h$)
Russia (Moscow): $+3^h$ (no DST)
Georgia: $+4^h$ (no DST)

Africa/Asia

South Africa, Namibia: $+2^h$ (no DST)
Kenya: $+3^h$ (no DST)
Egypt: $+2^h$ (no DST)
Israel: $+2^h$ (DST March 29 to Oct 26, $+3^h$)
India: $+5\frac{1}{2}^h$ (no DST)
Philippines, China: $+8^h$ (no DST)
Japan, Korea: $+9^h$ (no DST)

Australia/New Zealand

Western Australia: $+8^h$ (no DST)
Northern Territory: $+9\frac{1}{2}^h$ (no DST)
South Australia: $+9\frac{1}{2}^h$ (DST to April 6 and from Oct 6, $+10\frac{1}{2}^h$)
Queensland: $+10^h$ (no DST)
ACT, NSW, Victoria, Tasmania: $+10^h$ (DST to April 6 & from Oct 6, $+11^h$)
New Zealand: $+12^h$ (DST to April 6 and from Sep 29, $+13^h$)

North America

Newfoundland Standard Time: $-3\frac{1}{2}^h$ (DST March 10 to Nov 2, $-2\frac{1}{2}^h$)
Atlantic Standard Time: -4^h (DST March 10 to Nov 2, -3^h)
Eastern Standard Time: -5^h (DST March 10 to Nov 2, -4^h)
Central Standard Time: -6^h (DST March 10 to Nov 2, -5^h, except Saskatchewan with no DST)
Mountain Standard Time: -7^h (DST March 10 to Nov 2, -6^h, except AZ with no DST)
Pacific Standard Time: -8^h (DST March 10 to Nov 2, -7^h)
Alaska Standard Time: -9^h (DST March 10 to Nov 2, -8^h)
Hawaii Standard Time: -10^h (no DST)
Mexico (mostly CST): -6^h (DST April 7 to Oct 26, -5^h)

South America

Argentina: -3^h (no DST)
Brazil (Brasilia): -3^h (no DST)
Chile: -4^h (DST to April 6 and from Sep 8, -3^h)
Columbia, Peru: -5^h (no DST)

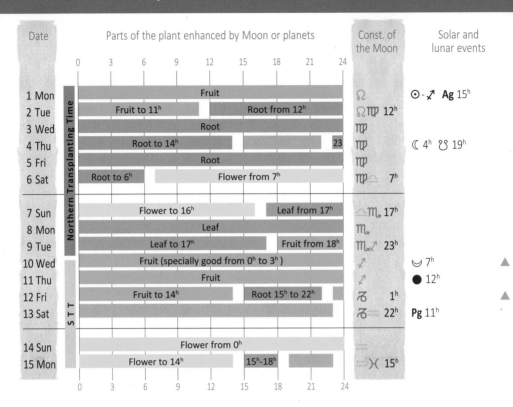

Date	Parts of the plant enhanced by Moon or planets	Const. of the Moon	Solar and lunar events
1 Mon	Fruit	♌	☉-♐ **Ag** 15ʰ
2 Tue	Fruit to 11ʰ / Root from 12ʰ	♌♍ 12ʰ	
3 Wed	Root	♍	
4 Thu	Root to 14ʰ — 23	♍	☾ 4ʰ ☋ 19ʰ
5 Fri	Root	♍	
6 Sat	Root to 6ʰ / Flower from 7ʰ	♍♎ 7ʰ	
7 Sun	Flower to 16ʰ / Leaf from 17ʰ	♎♏ 17ʰ	
8 Mon	Leaf	♏	
9 Tue	Leaf to 17ʰ / Fruit from 18ʰ	♏♐ 23ʰ	
10 Wed	Fruit (specially good from 0ʰ to 3ʰ)	♐	☋ 7ʰ
11 Thu	Fruit	♐	● 12ʰ
12 Fri	Fruit to 14ʰ / Root 15ʰ to 22ʰ	♑ 1ʰ	
13 Sat		♑♒ 22ʰ	**Pg** 11ʰ
14 Sun	Flower from 0ʰ	♒	
15 Mon	Flower to 14ʰ / 15ʰ-18ʰ	♒♓ 15ʰ	

Northern Transplanting Time

STT

Transplanting Time
(time of descending Moon in northern hemisphere)
Dec 27 to Jan 10 5ʰ and Jan 23 6ʰ to Feb 6

Leaf times
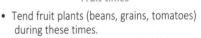
• Tend leafy plants (like lettuce) during these times.
• Sow winter lettuce and leeks in a greenhouse, or in warm regions in pots.

Root times

• Tend root plants (carrots, potatoes) during these times.
• Sow turnips in a greenhouse.

Fruit times

• Tend fruit plants (beans, grains, tomatoes) during these times.
• Plant bare-root fruit trees and soft-fruit shrubs on unfrozen soil.
• The Transplanting Time (to Jan 10 5ʰ and from Jan 23 6ʰ) is a good time for pruning **fruit trees, vines and hedges.** Fruit and Flower times are preferred for this work. Avoid unfavourable times.

Flower times
• Tend flowering plants (broccoli, roses) during these times.
• Sow cauliflower in warm regions in pots.
• Plant flowering shrubs.

Date	Planetary aspects (**Bold** = visible to naked eye)
1	
2	☾ ☍ ♆ 15ʰ
3	
4	
5	
6	☾ ☍ ♃ 0ʰ
7	☾ ☍ ☊ 1ʰ
8	☾ ☌ ♀ 19ʰ
9	☾ ☌ ☿ 18ʰ
10	☉ △ ☊ 0ʰ ☾ ☌ ♂ 9ʰ
11	
12	☽ ☌ ♇ 3ʰ ♂ △ ♃ 11ʰ
13	
14	☽ ☌ ♄ 11ʰ
15	☽ ☌ ♆ 21ʰ

Planet positions in zodiac

☿	Mercury	♏ 13 ♐ (R 2 D)
♀	Venus	♏
♂	Mars	♏ 2 ♐
♃	Jupiter	♈
♄	Saturn	♒
⛢	Uranus	♈ (R)
♆	Neptune	♓
♇	Pluto	♑

Planet (naked eye) visibility

Evening:
  Jupiter, Saturn

All night:
  —

Morning:
  Mercury, Venus

♓ Pisces	♈ Aries	♉ Taurus	♊ Gemini	♋ Cancer	♌ Leo
♍ Virgo	♎ Libra	♏ Scorpio	♐ Sagittarius	♑ Capricorn	♒ Aquarius

NB: All zodiac symbols refer to astronomical constellations, not astrological signs (see p. 10).

Milk processing

When **milk processing** it is best to avoid unfavourable times. This applies to both butter and cheese making. Milk which has been produced at Fruit times yields the highest butterfat content. This is also the case on days with a tendency for thunderstorms. Times of perigee (**Pg**) are almost always unfavourable for milk processing and even yoghurt will not turn out well. Starter cultures from such days decay rapidly and it is advisable to produce double the amount the day before. Milk loves Flower and Fruit times best of all. Leaf times are unsuitable.

Southern hemisphere

Southern Transplanting Time
Jan 10 9ʰ to Jan 23 2ʰ

Harvest time for seeds (Avoid unfavourable times)
- **Fruit seeds:** at Fruit times.
- **Flower seeds:** at Flower times.
- **Leaf seeds:** at Leaf times.
- **Root seeds:** at Root times.

Notes

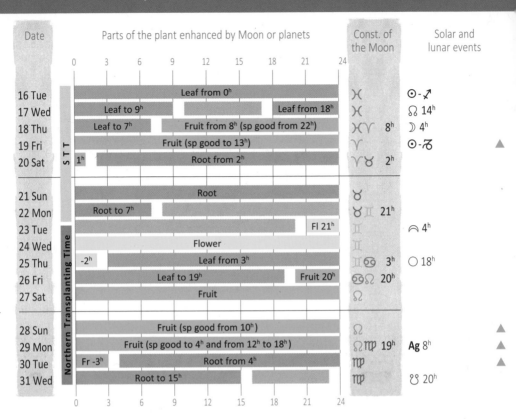

Date	Parts of the plant enhanced by Moon or planets	Const. of the Moon	Solar and lunar events
16 Tue	Leaf from 0ʰ	♓	☉-♐
17 Wed	Leaf to 9ʰ / Leaf from 18ʰ	♓	♋ 14ʰ
18 Thu	Leaf to 7ʰ / Fruit from 8ʰ (sp good from 22ʰ)	♓♈ 8ʰ	☽ 4ʰ
19 Fri	Fruit (sp good to 13ʰ)	♈	☉-♑ ▲
20 Sat	1ʰ Root from 2ʰ	♈♉ 2ʰ	
21 Sun	Root	♉	
22 Mon	Root to 7ʰ	♉♊ 21ʰ	
23 Tue	Fl 21ʰ	♊	⌒ 4ʰ
24 Wed	Flower	♊	
25 Thu	-2ʰ Leaf from 3ʰ	♊♋ 3ʰ	○ 18ʰ
26 Fri	Leaf to 19ʰ / Fruit 20ʰ	♋♌ 20ʰ	
27 Sat	Fruit	♌	
28 Sun	Fruit (sp good from 10ʰ)	♌	▲
29 Mon	Fruit (sp good to 4ʰ and from 12ʰ to 18ʰ)	♌♍ 19ʰ	Ag 8ʰ ▲
30 Tue	Fr -3ʰ Root from 4ʰ	♍	▲
31 Wed	Root to 15ʰ	♍	♋ 20ʰ

(Left side vertical labels: STT; Northern Transplanting Time)

Transplanting Time
(time of descending Moon in northern hemisphere)
Jan 23 6ʰ to Feb 6

Leaf times

- Tend leafy plants (like lettuce) during these times.
- Sow lettuce and cabbage in greenhouse.

Root times

- Tend root plants (carrots, potatoes) during these times.
- In mild areas plant garlic.

Fruit times

- Tend fruit plants (beans, grains, tomatoes) during these times.
- The Transplanting Time (from Jan 23 6ʰ to Feb 6) is a good time for pruning **fruit trees, vines and hedges.** Fruit and Flower times are preferred for this work. Avoid unfavourable times.
- In mild regions sow aubergines (eggplant) and chilli peppers.

Flower times

- Tend flowering plants (broccoli, roses) during these times.
- Prune **vines, fruit trees and hedges** – see Fruit times above.
- In mild regions (or a greenhouse) sow begonias and cannas.

Date	Planetary aspects (**Bold** = visible to naked eye)
16	
17	
18	☽☌♃ 19ʰ
19	☿△♃ 10ʰ ☽☌♁ 18ʰ
20	☉☌♇ 14ʰ
21	
22	☽☍♀ 21ʰ
23	☿♋ 8ʰ ☽☍♀ 21ʰ
24	☽☍♂ 2ʰ
25	☽☌♇ 8ʰ
26	
27	☿☌♂ 15ʰ
28	☾☍♄ 7ʰ ☿△♁ 21ʰ
29	♀△♃ 1ʰ ☾☍♆ 23ʰ
30	♂△♁ 0ʰ
31	

Planet positions in zodiac

☿	Mercury	♐
♀	Venus	♏ 22 ♐
♂	Mars	♐
♃	Jupiter	♈
♄	Saturn	♒
♁	Uranus	♈ (R 27 D)
♆	Neptune	♓
♇	Pluto	♑

Planet (naked eye) visibility

Evening:
Jupiter, Saturn

All night:
–

Morning:
Mercury (to Jan 28), Venus

♓ Pisces	♈ Aries	♉ Taurus	♊ Gemini	♋ Cancer	♌ Leo
♍ Virgo	♎ Libra	♏ Scorpio	♐ Sagittarius	♑ Capricorn	♒ Aquarius

Control pests
(see p. 74 for details)

- Burn feathers or skins of **warm blooded pests** from Jan 20 2ʰ to Jan 22 6ʰ. *The burning (and grinding) should be completed by Jan 22 6ʰ.*

Notes

Southern hemisphere

Southern Transplanting Time
Jan 10 to Jan 23 2ʰ

Harvest time for seeds *(Avoid unfavourable times)*
- **Fruit seeds:** at Fruit times.
- **Flower seeds:** at Flower times.
- **Leaf seeds:** at Leaf times.
- **Root seeds:** at Root times.

Control slugs from Jan 25 3ʰ to Jan 26 19ʰ (see p. 74 for details)

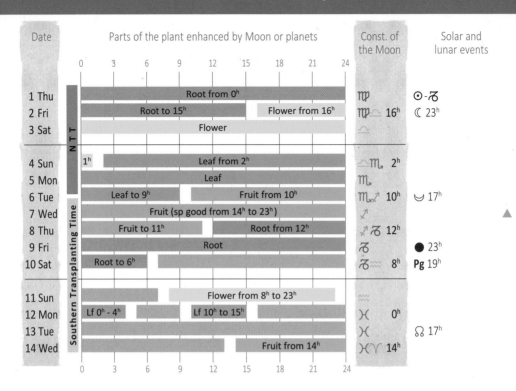

Date	Parts of the plant enhanced by Moon or planets	Const. of the Moon	Solar and lunar events
1 Thu	Root from 0ʰ	♍	☉-♑
2 Fri	Root to 15ʰ — Flower from 16ʰ	♍ ♎ 16ʰ	☾ 23ʰ
3 Sat	Flower	♎	
4 Sun	1ʰ — Leaf from 2ʰ	♎ ♏ 2ʰ	
5 Mon	Leaf	♏	
6 Tue	Leaf to 9ʰ — Fruit from 10ʰ	♏ ♐ 10ʰ	☋ 17ʰ
7 Wed	Fruit (sp good from 14ʰ to 23ʰ)	♐	
8 Thu	Fruit to 11ʰ — Root from 12ʰ	♐ ♑ 12ʰ	
9 Fri	Root	♑	● 23ʰ
10 Sat	Root to 6ʰ	♑ ♒ 8ʰ	Pg 19ʰ
11 Sun	Flower from 8ʰ to 23ʰ	♒	
12 Mon	Lf 0ʰ – 4ʰ — Lf 10ʰ to 15ʰ	♓ 0ʰ	
13 Tue		♓	☊ 17ʰ
14 Wed	Fruit from 14ʰ	♓ ♈ 14ʰ	

Transplanting Time
(time of descending Moon in northern hemisphere)
Jan 23 to Feb 6 15ʰ and Feb 19 11ʰ to March 4

Fruit times
- Tend fruit plants (beans, grains, tomatoes) during these times.
- **Vines, fruit trees and shrubs** can be pruned during Transplanting Time to Feb 6 15ʰ and from Feb 19 11ʰ. Flower and Fruit times are preferred. Avoid unfavourable times.

Leaf times
- Tend leafy plants (like lettuce) during these times.
- Transplant lettuce and cabbage during Transplanting Time.

Root times
- Tend root plants (carrots, potatoes) during these times.

Flower times
- Tend flowering plants (broccoli, roses) during these times.
- Prune **vines, fruit trees and shrubs** – see Fruit times above.
- Take **willow cuttings for hedges and fences** *outside* Transplanting Time (Feb 6 19ʰ to Feb 19 7ʰ). In warm areas *during* Transplanting Time to avoid too strong a sap current.

Date	Planetary aspects
	(**Bold** = visible to naked eye)
1	
2	☾☌☍♃ 11ʰ
3	☾☌☍⛢ 10ʰ
4	
5	☿☌♇ 13ʰ
6	
7	**☾☌♀ 20ʰ** ♀△⛢ 21ʰ
8	**☾☌♂ 8ʰ** ☾☌♇ 15ʰ ☾☌☿ 23ʰ
9	
10	
11	☽☌♄ 2ʰ
12	☽●♆ 7ʰ
13	
14	♀☍ 0ʰ ♂☌♇ 6ʰ

Planet positions in zodiac

☿	Mercury	♐ 4♑
♀	Venus	♐
♂	Mars	♐ 11♑
♃	Jupiter	♈
♄	Saturn	♒
⛢	Uranus	♈
♆	Neptune	♓
♇	Pluto	♑

Planet (naked eye) visibility

Evening:
Jupiter, Saturn

All night:
–

Morning:
Venus

♓ Pisces	♈ Aries	♉ Taurus	♊ Gemini	♋ Cancer	♌ Leo
♍ Virgo	♎ Libra	♏ Scorpio	♐ Sagittarius	♑ Capricorn	♒ Aquarius

NB: All zodiac symbols refer to astronomical constellations, not astrological signs (see p. 10).

Notes

Southern hemisphere

Southern Transplanting Time
Feb 6 19ʰ to Feb 19 7ʰ

Harvest time for seeds (Avoid unfavourable times)
- **Fruit seeds:** at Fruit times.
- **Flower seeds:** at Flower times.
- **Leaf seeds:** at Leaf times.
- **Root seeds:** at Root times.

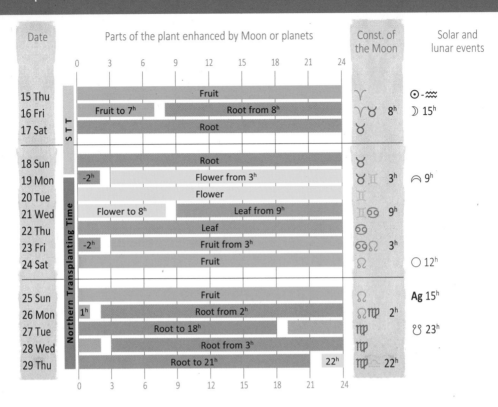

Date	Parts of the plant enhanced by Moon or planets	Const. of the Moon	Solar and lunar events
15 Thu	Fruit	♈	☉ - ♒
16 Fri	Fruit to 7ʰ / Root from 8ʰ	♈♉ 8ʰ	☽ 15ʰ
17 Sat	Root	♉	
18 Sun	Root	♉	
19 Mon	-2ʰ / Flower from 3ʰ	♉♊ 3ʰ	⌒ 9ʰ
20 Tue	Flower	♊	
21 Wed	Flower to 8ʰ / Leaf from 9ʰ	♊♋ 9ʰ	
22 Thu	Leaf	♋	
23 Fri	-2ʰ / Fruit from 3ʰ	♋♌ 3ʰ	
24 Sat	Fruit	♌	○ 12ʰ
25 Sun	Fruit	♌	Ag 15ʰ
26 Mon	1ʰ / Root from 2ʰ	♌♍ 2ʰ	
27 Tue	Root to 18ʰ	♍	☋ 23ʰ
28 Wed	Root from 3ʰ	♍	
29 Thu	Root to 21ʰ / 22ʰ	♍♎ 22ʰ	

(Left vertical labels: S T T; Northern Transplanting Time)

Time axis: 0 3 6 9 12 15 18 21 24

Transplanting Time

(time of descending Moon in northern hemisphere)

Feb 19 11ʰ to March 4

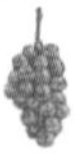

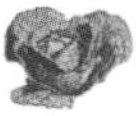

Fruit times

- Tend fruit plants (beans, grains, tomatoes) during these times.
- **Vines, fruit trees and shrubs** can be pruned during Transplanting Time (Feb 19 11ʰ to March 4). Flower and Fruit times are preferred. Avoid unfavourable times.
- Sow tomatoes, aubergines (eggplant) and chilli peppers in a greenhouse.

Leaf times

- Tend leafy plants (like lettuce) during these times.
- Transplant lettuce and cabbage during Transplanting Time.

Flower times

- Tend flowering plants (broccoli, roses) during these times.
- Prune **vines, fruit trees and shrubs** – see Fruit times above.
- Sow broccoli.
- Take **willow cuttings for hedges and fences** *outside* Transplanting Time (to Feb 19 7ʰ). In warm areas *during* Transplanting Time to avoid too strong a sap current.

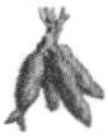

Root times

- Tend root plants (carrots, potatoes) during these times.
- Plant shallots and onions.

Date	Planetary aspects (**Bold** = visible to naked eye)
15	☽︎☌♃ 7ʰ
16	☽︎☌♅ 0ʰ
17	♀☌♇ 9ʰ
18	
19	
20	
21	☽︎☍♇ 16ʰ
22	☽︎☍♀ 3ʰ ☽︎☍♂ 3ʰ ♀☌♂ 7ʰ
23	
24	☽︎☍☿ 5ʰ ☾☍♄ 20ʰ
25	
26	☾☍♆ 8ʰ
27	
28	☉☌♀ 9ʰ ☿☌♄ 15ʰ ☉☌♄ 21ʰ
29	

Planet positions in zodiac

☿	Mercury	♑ 21 ♒
♀	Venus	♐ 15 ♑
♂	Mars	♑
♃	Jupiter	♈
♄	Saturn	♒
♅	Uranus	♈
♆	Neptune	♓
♇	Pluto	♑

Planet (naked eye) visibility

Evening:
Jupiter, Saturn (to Feb 15)

All night:
–

Morning:
Venus

♓ Pisces	♈ Aries	♉ Taurus	♊ Gemini	♋ Cancer	♌ Leo
♍ Virgo	♎ Libra	♏ Scorpio	♐ Sagittarius	♑ Capricorn	♒ Aquarius

NB: All zodiac symbols refer to astronomical constellations, not astrological signs (see p. 10).

Notes

Southern hemisphere

Southern Transplanting Time
Feb 6 to Feb 19 7ʰ

Harvest time for seeds (*Avoid unfavourable times*)
- **Fruit seeds:** at Fruit times.
- **Flower seeds:** at Flower times.
- **Leaf seeds:** at Leaf times.
- **Root seeds:** at Root times.

Control slugs from Feb 21 9ʰ to Feb 23 2ʰ (see p. 74 for details)

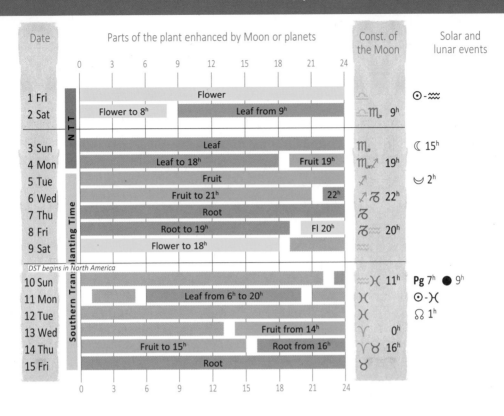

Date	Parts of the plant enhanced by Moon or planets	Const. of the Moon	Solar and lunar events
1 Fri	Flower	♎ ☽	☉-♒
2 Sat	Flower to 8ʰ / Leaf from 9ʰ	♎ ♏ 9ʰ	
3 Sun	Leaf	♏	☾ 15ʰ
4 Mon	Leaf to 18ʰ / Fruit 19ʰ	♏ ♐ 19ʰ	
5 Tue	Fruit	♐	☌ 2ʰ
6 Wed	Fruit to 21ʰ / 22ʰ	♐ ♑ 22ʰ	
7 Thu	Root	♑	
8 Fri	Root to 19ʰ / Fl 20ʰ	♑ ♒ 20ʰ	
9 Sat	Flower to 18ʰ	♒	
10 Sun		♒ ♓ 11ʰ	Pg 7ʰ ● 9ʰ
11 Mon	Leaf from 6ʰ to 20ʰ	♓	☉-♓
12 Tue		♓	☋ 1ʰ
13 Wed	Fruit from 14ʰ	♈ 0ʰ	
14 Thu	Fruit to 15ʰ / Root from 16ʰ	♈ ♉ 16ʰ	
15 Fri	Root	♉	

NTT (Northern Transplanting Time)

Southern Transplanting Time

DST begins in North America

Transplanting Time
(time of descending Moon in northern hemisphere)
Feb 19 to March 4 24ʰ
and March 17 17ʰ to April 1 7ʰ

Leaf times
- Tend leafy plants (like lettuce) during these times.
- Transplant spinach and lettuce during Transplanting Time.

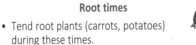

Root times
- Tend root plants (carrots, potatoes) during these times.
- Sow carrots, radishes and turnips.
- Plant artichokes, horseradish and early potatoes.

Fruit times
- Tend fruit plants (beans, grains, tomatoes) during these times.
- Prune fruit trees and shrubs.
- **Cuttings for grafting:** cut outside Transplanting Time during ascending Moon. For fruit trees and shrubs, March 5 4ʰ to March 6 21ʰ, or March 13 14ʰ to March 14 15ʰ.
- In warm areas plant cucumbers and tomatoes in pots.

Flower times
- Tend flowering plants (broccoli, roses) during these times.
- **Cuttings for grafting:** cut outside Transplanting Time during ascending Moon. For flowering shrubs, March 8 20ʰ to March 9 18ʰ.

Date	Planetary aspects (**Bold** = visible to naked eye)
1	☾☍♃ 2^{h} ☾☍⛢ 18^{h}
2	
3	
4	
5	
6	
7	☾☌♇ 3^{h}
8	☾☌♂ 7^{h} ☿☌♆ 15^{h} **☾☌♀ 19^{h}**
9	☾☌♄ 18^{h}
10	☽●♆ 20^{h}
11	☽●☿ 3^{h}
12	
13	☿☊ 1^{h} **☽☌♃ 23^{h}**
14	☽☌⛢ 10^{h}
15	

Planet positions in zodiac

- ☿ Mercury ♒ 5 ♓
- ♀ Venus ♑ 9 ♒
- ♂ Mars ♑
- ♃ Jupiter ♈
- ♄ Saturn ♒
- ⛢ Uranus ♈
- ♆ Neptune ♓
- ♇ Pluto ♑

Planet (naked eye) visibility

Evening: Mercury (from March 12), Jupiter

All night: –

Morning: Venus

♓ Pisces ♈ Aries ♉ Taurus ♊ Gemini ♋ Cancer ♌ Leo
♍ Virgo ♎ Libra ♏ Scorpio ♐ Sagittarius ♑ Capricorn ♒ Aquarius

NB: All zodiac symbols refer to astronomical constellations, not astrological signs (see p. 10).

Control pests
(see p. 74 for details)

- **Clothes and wax moths:** ash from March 13 0^{h} to March 14 15^{h}.

Beekeeping

Remove anti-bird nets and mouse guards to enable clearing flights between March 9 and 11.

Biodynamic preparations

Pick **dandelions** in March or April in the mornings during Flower times. The flowers should not be quite open in the centre. Dry them on paper in the shade, not in bright sunlight. Once dried they can be stored until suitably encased and buried in the ground.

Southern hemisphere

Southern Transplanting Time
March 5 4^{h} to March 17 13^{h}

Harvest time for seeds *(Avoid unfavourable times)*

- **Fruit seeds:** at Fruit times.
- **Flower seeds:** at Flower times.
- **Leaf seeds:** at Leaf times.
- **Root seeds:** at Root times.

Tip

Want to know more about biodynamic preparations?

- See ‘Biodynamic preparations’, p. 73.

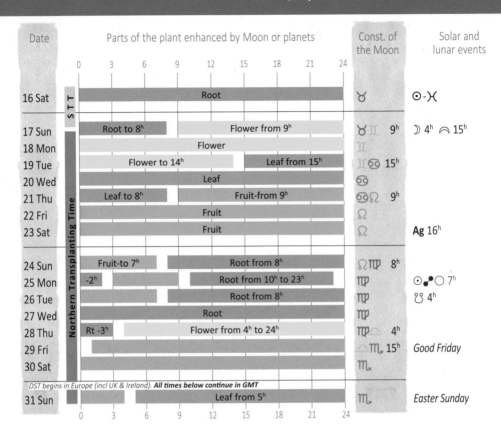

Calendar chart: "Parts of the plant enhanced by Moon or planets" (hours 0–24), "Const. of the Moon", and "Solar and lunar events".

Date	Parts of the plant enhanced by Moon or planets	Const. of the Moon	Solar and lunar events
16 Sat	Root	♉	☉-♓
17 Sun	Root to 8ʰ / Flower from 9ʰ	♉ ♊ 9ʰ	☽ 4ʰ ♑ 15ʰ
18 Mon	Flower	♊	
19 Tue	Flower to 14ʰ / Leaf from 15ʰ	♊ ♋ 15ʰ	
20 Wed	Leaf	♋	
21 Thu	Leaf to 8ʰ / Fruit-from 9ʰ	♋ ♌ 9ʰ	
22 Fri	Fruit	♌	
23 Sat	Fruit	♌	Ag 16ʰ
24 Sun	Fruit-to 7ʰ / Root from 8ʰ	♌ ♍ 8ʰ	☉ ● ○ 7ʰ
25 Mon	-2ʰ / Root from 10ʰ to 23ʰ	♍	
26 Tue	Root from 8ʰ	♍	☊ 4ʰ
27 Wed	Root	♍	
28 Thu	Rt -3ʰ / Flower from 4ʰ to 24ʰ	♍ ♎ 4ʰ	
29 Fri		♎ ♏ 15ʰ	*Good Friday*
30 Sat		♏	
31 Sun	Leaf from 5ʰ	♏	*Easter Sunday*

Left margin: s T T · Northern Transplanting Time

DST begins in Europe (incl UK & Ireland). **All times below continue in GMT**

Transplanting Time
(time of descending Moon in northern hemisphere)

March 17 17ʰ to April 1 7ʰ

Good Friday and Easter
Maria Thun's research has shown that planting and other work is unfavourable from Good Friday to dawn on Easter Sunday, *local time.*

Leaf times

- Tend leafy plants (like lettuce) during these times.
- Sow cabbage, Brussels sprouts, endives.

Fruit times

- Tend fruit plants (beans, grains, tomatoes) during these times.
- Sow melon seeds in pots.
- Plant strawberries

Root times

- Tend root plants during these times.
- Sow parsnips.
- Plant potatoes.

Flower times

- Tend flowering plants (broccoli, roses) during these times.

Date

Planetary aspects
(**Bold** = visible to naked eye)

Planet positions in zodiac		
☿	Mercury	♓
♀	Venus	♒ 29 ♓
♂	Mars	♑ 18 ♒
♃	Jupiter	♈
♄	Saturn	♒
♅	Uranus	♈
♆	Neptune	♓
♇	Pluto	♑

16

17   ☉☌♆ 11ʰ
18
19   ☽☌♇ 23ʰ
20
21   ♀☌♄ 23ʰ
22   ☽☍♂ 7ʰ
23   ☽☍♄ 9ʰ   ☽☍♀ 13ʰ

24   ☽☍♆ 16ʰ
25
26   ☾☍☿ 23ʰ
27
28   ☾☍♃ 18ʰ
29   ☾☍♅ 2ʰ
30

31

Planet (naked eye) visibility

Evening:
    Mercury, Jupiter

All night:
    –

Morning:
    Venus (to March 20)

NB: All zodiac symbols refer to astronomical constellations, not astrological signs (see p. 10).

Control pests
(see p. 74 for details)
- **Slugs:** ash from March 19 15ʰ to March 21 8ʰ.

Biodynamic preparations
Pick **dandelions** in March or April in the mornings during Flower times. The flowers should not be quite open in the centre. Dry them on paper in the shade, not in bright sunlight. Once dried they can be stored until suitably encased and buried in the ground.

Southern hemisphere
Southern Transplanting Time
March 5 to March 17 13ʰ

Harvest time for seeds *(Avoid unfavourable times)*
- **Fruit seeds:** at Fruit times.
- **Flower seeds:** at Flower times.
- **Leaf seeds:** at Leaf times.
- **Root seeds:** at Root times.

Beekeeping
Willow cuttings for **pollen production** are best cut from March 17 17ʰ to March 19 14ʰ, and for **honey flow** from March 21 9ʰ to March 24 7ʰ.

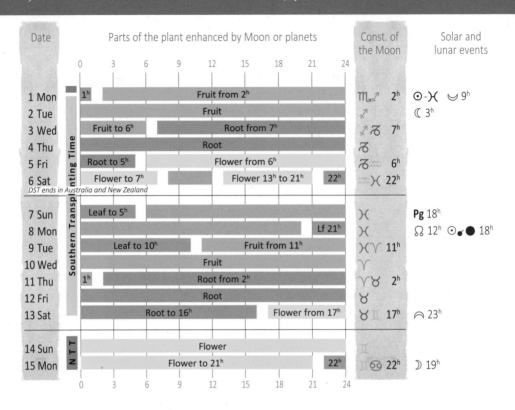

Date	Parts of the plant enhanced by Moon or planets	Const. of the Moon	Solar and lunar events
1 Mon	1ʰ · Fruit from 2ʰ	♏♐ 2ʰ	☉–♓ ☋ 9ʰ
2 Tue	Fruit	♐	☾ 3ʰ
3 Wed	Fruit to 6ʰ · Root from 7ʰ	♐♑ 7ʰ	
4 Thu	Root	♑	
5 Fri	Root to 5ʰ · Flower from 6ʰ	♑≈ 6ʰ	
6 Sat	Flower to 7ʰ · Flower 13ʰ to 21ʰ · 22ʰ	≈♓ 22ʰ	
	DST ends in Australia and New Zealand		
7 Sun	Leaf to 5ʰ	♓	Pg 18ʰ
8 Mon	Lf 21ʰ	♓	☊ 12ʰ ☉☽● 18ʰ
9 Tue	Leaf to 10ʰ · Fruit from 11ʰ	♓♈ 11ʰ	
10 Wed	Fruit	♈	
11 Thu	1ʰ · Root from 2ʰ	♈♉ 2ʰ	
12 Fri	Root	♉	
13 Sat	Root to 16ʰ · Flower from 17ʰ	♉♊ 17ʰ	⌢ 23ʰ
14 Sun	Flower	♊	
15 Mon	Flower to 21ʰ · 22ʰ	♊♋ 22ʰ	☽ 19ʰ

(Left sidebar: *Southern Transplanting Time* / *NTT*)

Transplanting Time
(time of descending Moon in northern hemisphere)
March 17 to April 1 7ʰ
and April 14 1ʰ to April 28 12ʰ

Leaf times

- Tend leafy plants (like lettuce) during these times.

Root times

- Tend root plants (carrots, potatoes) during these times.
- Transplant **seed potatoes** for next year with Moon in Aries, from April 9 11ʰ to April 11 1ʰ, avoiding unfavourable times.
- Sow turnips, swede (rutabaga).

Fruit times

- Tend fruit plants (beans, grains, tomatoes) during these times.
- **Graft fruiting shrubs** *outside* Transplanting Times: April 1 11ʰ to April 3 6ʰ or April 9 11ʰ to April 11 1ʰ
- Sow courgettes (zucchini) and squash.

Flower times

- Tend flowering plants (broccoli, roses) during these times.
- Plant annuals and flowering shrubs.
- **Graft flowering shrubs** *outside* Transplanting Times: April 5 6ʰ to April 6 21ʰ, avoiding unfavourable times..
- Prune flowering shrubs that have flowered.

Date

Planetary aspects
(**Bold** = visible to naked eye)

1	
2	
3	☽ ☌ ♇ 12ʰ ♀ ☌ ♆ 13ʰ
4	
5	
6	☽ ☌ ♂ 5ʰ ☽ • ♄ 10ʰ
7	☽ • ♆ 8ʰ ☽ • ♀ 16ʰ
8	
9	☽ ☌ ☿ 3ʰ
10	☽ ☌ ♃ 19ʰ ♂ ☌ ♄ 21ʰ ☽ ☌ ♅ 22ʰ
11	☉ ☌ ☿ 23ʰ
12	
13	
14	
15	

Planet positions in zodiac

☿ Mercury ♓ (1 R)
♀ Venus ♓
♂ Mars ♒
♃ Jupiter ♈
♄ Saturn ♒
♅ Uranus ♈
♆ Neptune ♓
♇ Pluto ♑

Planet (naked eye) visibility

Evening:
  Mercury (to April 4), Jupiter

All night:
  –

Morning:
  –

♓ Pisces	♈ Aries	♉ Taurus	♊ Gemini	♋ Cancer	♌ Leo
♍ Virgo	♎ Libra	♏ Scorpio	♐ Sagittarius	♑ Capricorn	♒ Aquarius

NB: All zodiac symbols refer to astronomical constellations, not astrological signs (see p. 10).

Control pests
(see p. 74 for details)

- **Slugs:** ash from April 15 22ʰ to April 17 14ʰ.
  Clothes and wax moths: ash from April 9 11ʰ to April 11 1ʰ.

Biodynamic preparations

Pick **dandelions** in March or April in the mornings during Flower times. The flowers should not be quite open in the centre. Dry them on paper in the shade, not in bright sunlight. Once dried they can be stored until suitably encased and buried in the ground.

Southern hemisphere

Southern Transplanting Time
April 1 11ʰ to April 13 21ʰ and
April 28 16ʰ to May 11

Harvest time for seeds (*Avoid unfavourable times*)
- **Fruit seeds:** at Fruit times.
- **Flower seeds:** at Flower times.
- **Leaf seeds:** at Leaf times.
- **Root seeds:** at Root times.

Notes

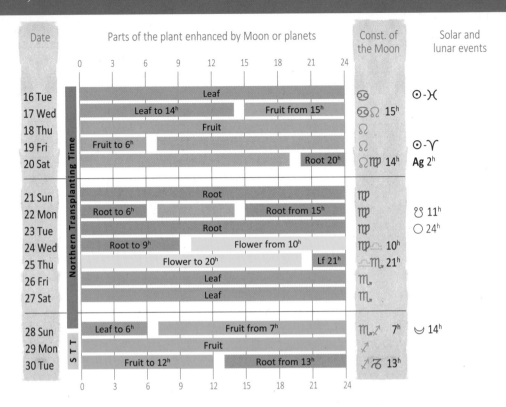

Date	Parts of the plant enhanced by Moon or planets	Const. of the Moon	Solar and lunar events
16 Tue	Leaf	♋	☉-♓
17 Wed	Leaf to 14ʰ — Fruit from 15ʰ	♋♌ 15ʰ	
18 Thu	Fruit	♌	
19 Fri	Fruit to 6ʰ	♌	☉-♈
20 Sat	Root 20ʰ	♌♍ 14ʰ	**Ag** 2ʰ
21 Sun	Root	♍	
22 Mon	Root to 6ʰ — Root from 15ʰ	♍	☍ 11ʰ
23 Tue	Root	♍	○ 24ʰ
24 Wed	Root to 9ʰ — Flower from 10ʰ	♍♎ 10ʰ	
25 Thu	Flower to 20ʰ — Lf 21ʰ	♎♏ 21ʰ	
26 Fri	Leaf	♏	
27 Sat	Leaf	♏	
28 Sun	Leaf to 6ʰ — Fruit from 7ʰ	♏♐ 7ʰ	☾ 14ʰ
29 Mon	Fruit	♐	
30 Tue	Fruit to 12ʰ — Root from 13ʰ	♐♑ 13ʰ	

Northern Transplanting Time (left margin, 16–27); *STT* (left margin, 28–30)

Transplanting Time
(time of descending Moon in northern hemisphere)

April 14 to April 28 12ʰ

Leaf times

- Tend leafy plants (like lettuce) during these times.
- Mow lawns if you want to encourage vigorous growth of the grass.
- Transplant chicory, endives, cabbage, Brussels sprouts during Transplanting Times.

Root times

- Tend root plants (carrots, potatoes) during these times.
- Sow salsify and parsnips.

Fruit times

- Tend fruit plants (beans, grains, tomatoes) during these times.
- **Graft fruiting shrubs** *outside* Transplanting Times: April 28 16ʰ to April 30 12ʰ, avoiding unfavourable times.
- Transplant aubergines (eggplant), tomatoes during Transplanting Times.

Flower times

- Tend flowering plants (broccoli, roses) during these times.
- Transplant cauliflowers and broccoli during Transplanting Times.
- Plant begonias, dahlias, gladiolas and other annual flowers.

Date	Planetary aspects (**Bold** = visible to naked eye)

Planet positions in zodiac

☿ Mercury ♓ (R 25 D)
♀ Venus ♓ 29 ♈
♂ Mars ♒ 19 ♓
♃ Jupiter ♈ 29 ♉
♄ Saturn ♒
♅ Uranus ♈
♆ Neptune ♓
♇ Pluto ♑

16	☽ ☍ ♇ 6ʰ
17	
18	
19	☿ ☌ ♀ 9ʰ ☽ ☍ ♄ 22ʰ
20	☿ ☋ 7ʰ ☽ ☍ ♂ 11ʰ
21	☽ ☍ ♆ 0ʰ ♃ ☌ ♅ 2ʰ
22	☽ ☍ ☿ 12ʰ ☽ ☍ ♀ 23ʰ
23	
24	
25	☾ ☍ ♅ 10ʰ ☾ ☍ ♃ 12ʰ
26	
27	
28	
29	♂ ☌ ♆ 5ʰ
30	☾ ☌ ♇ 19ʰ

Planet (naked eye) visibility

Evening:
   Jupiter

All night:
   –

Morning:
   Saturn (from April 23)

♓ Pisces	♈ Aries	♉ Taurus	♊ Gemini	♋ Cancer	♌ Leo
♍ Virgo	♎ Libra	♏ Scorpio	♐ Sagittarius	♑ Capricorn	♒ Aquarius

NB: All zodiac symbols refer to astronomical constellations, not astrological signs (see p. 10).

Control pests
(see p. 74 for details)

- **Slugs:** ash from April 15 22ʰ to April 17 14ʰ.
  Mole crickets: ash from April 25 21ʰ to April 28 6ʰ.

Biodynamic preparations

Pick **dandelions** in March or April in the mornings during Flower times. The flowers should not be quite open in the centre. Dry them on paper in the shade, not in bright sunlight. Once dried they can be stored until suitably encased and buried in the ground.

Southern hemisphere

Southern Transplanting Time
April 28 16ʰ to May 11

Harvest time for seeds (*Avoid unfavourable times*)
- **Fruit seeds:** at Fruit times.
- **Flower seeds:** at Flower times.
- **Leaf seeds:** at Leaf times.
- **Root seeds:** at Root times.

Notes

Date	Parts of the plant enhanced by Moon or planets	Const. of the Moon	Solar and lunar events
1 Wed	Root	♑	☉-♈ ☾ 11ʰ
2 Thu	Root to 12ʰ / Flower from 13ʰ	♑ ♒ 13ʰ	
3 Fri	Flower to 20ʰ	♒	
4 Sat	Fl 2ʰ - 6ʰ / Leaf 7ʰ to 16ʰ	♒ ♓ 7ʰ	
5 Sun	Leaf 5-9ʰ	♓	♌ 22ʰ **Pg 22ʰ**
6 Mon	Leaf 11ʰ to 20ʰ / Fr 21ʰ	♓ ♈ 21ʰ	
7 Tue	Fruit	♈	
8 Wed	Fruit to 12ʰ / Root from 13ʰ	♈ ♉ 13ʰ	● 3ʰ
9 Thu	Root	♉	*Ascension*
10 Fri	Root	♉	
11 Sat	1ʰ / Flower from 2ʰ	♉ ♊ 2ʰ	⌢ 8ʰ
12 Sun	Flower	♊	
13 Mon	Flower to 5ʰ / Leaf from 6ʰ	♊ ♋ 6ʰ	☉-♉
14 Tue	Leaf to 22ʰ	23	♋ ♌ 23ʰ	
15 Wed	Fruit	♌	☽ 12ʰ

Left margin: Southern Transplanting Time (1–11), NTT (12–15)

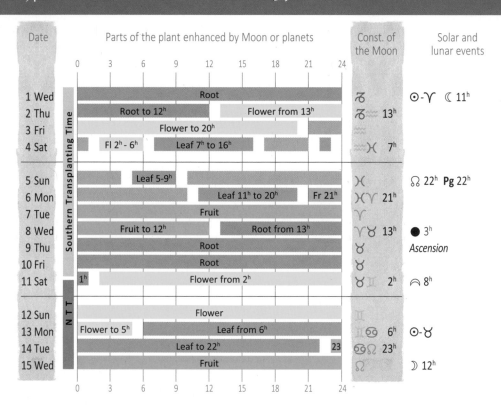

Leaf times
- Tend leafy plants (like lettuce) during these times.
- Plant aromatic herbs.
- Transplant cabbage during Transplanting Times.
- Sow lettuce, endives, parsley, chervil, kale.

Root times
- Tend root plants (carrots, potatoes) during these times.
- Sow beetroots (beets) and carrots.
- Transplant **seed potatoes** for next year when the Moon is in Aries, from May 6 21ʰ to May 8 12ʰ, avoiding unfavourable times.

Fruit times
- Tend fruit plants (beans, grains, tomatoes) during these times.
- **Graft fruiting shrubs** outside Transplanting Times: May 6 21ʰ to May 8 12ʰ.
- Sow beans, courgettes (zucchini), cucumbers.

Flower times
- Tend flowering plants (broccoli, roses) during these times.
- Sow cauliflower and broccoli.
- Cut **hay**.

Soil
The **soil warms up** on May 15.

Date		Planetary aspects
		(**Bold** = visible to naked eye)
1		
2		
3		$\mathbb{C}$ ☌ ♄ 23^h
4		$\mathbb{C}$ ☌ ♆ 19^h
5		$\mathbb{C}$ ☌ ♂ 2^h
6		$\mathbb{C}$ ☌ ☿ 6^h
7		$\mathbb{C}$ ☌ ♀ 14^h
8		☽ ☌ ♅ 11^h ☽ ☌ ♃ 17^h
9		
10		
11		
12		
13		☉ ☌ ♅ 9^h ☽ ☍ ♇ 15^h
14		
15		

Planet positions in zodiac

☿	Mercury	♓ 15 ♈
♀	Venus	♈
♂	Mars	♓
♃	Jupiter	♉
♄	Saturn	♒
♅	Uranus	♈
♆	Neptune	♓
♇	Pluto	♑ (2 R)

Planet (naked eye) visibility

Evening:
   Jupiter (to May 4)

All night:
   –

Morning:
   Saturn

♓ Pisces	♈ Aries	♉ Taurus	♊ Gemini	♋ Cancer	♌ Leo
♍ Virgo	♎ Libra	♏ Scorpio	♐ Sagittarius	♑ Capricorn	♒ Aquarius

NB: All zodiac symbols refer to astronomical constellations, not astrological signs (see p. 10).

Control pests
(see p. 74 for details)

- **Flies:** burn fly papers in the cow barn at Flower times.
- **Slugs:** ash from May 13 6^h to May 14 22^h.
- **Moths:** ash from May 4 7^h to May 6 20^h.
- **Ants** in the house: ash when the Moon is in Leo, May 14 23^h to May 17 20^h.
- **Chitinous insects, wheat weevil, Colorado beetle and varroa:** ash from May 8 13^h to May 11 1^h.

Beekeeping

- Begin **queen bee** rearing (grafting or larval transfer, comb insertion, cell punching) between May 11 2^h and May 13 5^h or at other Flower times.

Southern hemisphere

Southern Transplanting Time
April 28 to May 11 6^h and May 25 22^h to June 7

Notes

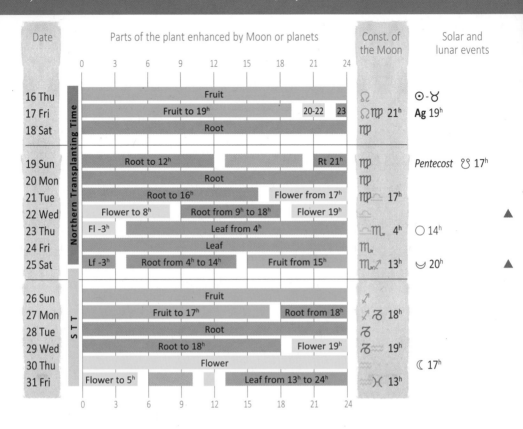

Date	Parts of the plant enhanced by Moon or planets	Const. of the Moon	Solar and lunar events
16 Thu	Fruit	♌	☉-♉
17 Fri	Fruit to 19ʰ 20-22 23	♌♍ 21ʰ	**Ag** 19ʰ
18 Sat	Root	♍	
19 Sun	Root to 12ʰ Rt 21ʰ	♍	*Pentecost* ☋ 17ʰ
20 Mon	Root	♍	
21 Tue	Root to 16ʰ Flower from 17ʰ	♍♎ 17ʰ	
22 Wed	Flower to 8ʰ Root from 9ʰ to 18ʰ Flower 19ʰ	♎	▲
23 Thu	Fl -3ʰ Leaf from 4ʰ	♎♏ 4ʰ	○ 14ʰ
24 Fri	Leaf	♏	
25 Sat	Lf -3ʰ Root from 4ʰ to 14ʰ Fruit from 15ʰ	♏♐ 13ʰ	☋ 20ʰ ▲
26 Sun	Fruit	♐	
27 Mon	Fruit to 17ʰ Root from 18ʰ	♐♑ 18ʰ	
28 Tue	Root	♑	
29 Wed	Root to 18ʰ Flower 19ʰ	♑♒ 19ʰ	
30 Thu	Flower	♒	☾ 17ʰ
31 Fri	Flower to 5ʰ Leaf from 13ʰ to 24ʰ	♒♓ 13ʰ	

Northern Transplanting Time (left of chart, rows 16–25). *S T T* (rows 26–31).

Transplanting Time
(time of descending Moon in northern hemisphere)
May 11 to May 25 18ʰ

Leaf times
- Tend leafy plants (like lettuce) during these times.
- Prune hedges.
- Transplant Brussels sprouts, celery, lettuce during Transplanting Times.
- Thin lettuce and chard.

Root times
- Tend root plants (carrots, potatoes) during these times.
- Transplant **table potatoes** during Transplanting Times.
- Sow winter radishes and carrots.

Fruit times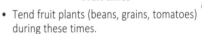
- Tend fruit plants (beans, grains, tomatoes) during these times.
- Prune suckers off tomatoes, cucumbers.
- Prune fruit trees after the fruit falls off.

Flower times
- Tend flowering plants (broccoli, roses) during these times.
- Cut **hay** between May 29 19ʰ and May 31 5ʰ, and at other Flower times.
- Layer climbing roses, clematis, honeysuckle.

Date	Planetary aspects (**Bold** = visible to naked eye)

Planet positions in zodiac

☿ Mercury ♈ 31 ♉
♀ Venus ♈ 18 ♉
♂ Mars ♓
♃ Jupiter ♉
♄ Saturn ♒
♅ Uranus ♈ 23 ♉
♆ Neptune ♓
♇ Pluto ♑ (R)

Date	Planetary aspects
16	
17	☽ ☍ ♄ 10ʰ
18	☽ ☍ ♆ 9ʰ ♀ ☌ ☊ 12ʰ ☉ ☌ ♃ 19ʰ
19	☽ ☍ ♂ 16ʰ
20	
21	☽ ☍ ☿ 14ʰ
22	☉ △ ♇ 15ʰ ☽ ☍ ☊ 20ʰ
23	☽ ☍ ♀ 7ʰ ☽ ☍ ♃ 7ʰ ♀ ☌ ♃ 9ʰ
24	
25	♀ △ ♇ 11ʰ
26	
27	
28	☾ ☌ ♇ 0ʰ
29	
30	
31	☿ ☌ ☊ 6ʰ ☾ ☌ ♄ 8ʰ

Planet (naked eye) visibility

Evening:
  –

All night:
  –

Morning:
  Mars (from May 29), Saturn

♓ Pisces   ♈ Aries   ♉ Taurus   ♊ Gemini   ♋ Cancer   ♌ Leo
♍ Virgo   ♎ Libra   ♏ Scorpio   ♐ Sagittarius   ♑ Capricorn   ♒ Aquarius

---

Control pests
(see p. 74 for details)

- **Flies:** burn fly papers in the cow barn at Flower times.
- **Ants** in the house: ash when the Moon is in Leo, May 14 23ʰ to May 17 20ʰ.
- **Mole crickets:** ash from May 23 4ʰ to May 25 3ʰ.

Beekeeping

- Begin **queen bee** rearing (grafting or larval transfer, comb insertion, cell punching) at Flower times.
- Possible **swarm time:** May 18 to June 16.

Southern hemisphere

Southern Transplanting Time
May 25 22ʰ to June 7

Biodynamic preparations

Preparations can be taken out of the ground after May 22 avoiding unfavourable times (best at Fruit or Flower times).

After dynamising for 1 hour **horn silica** preparation should be buried in ground after May 22 (avoiding unfavourable times), but not in the same hole as above preparations.

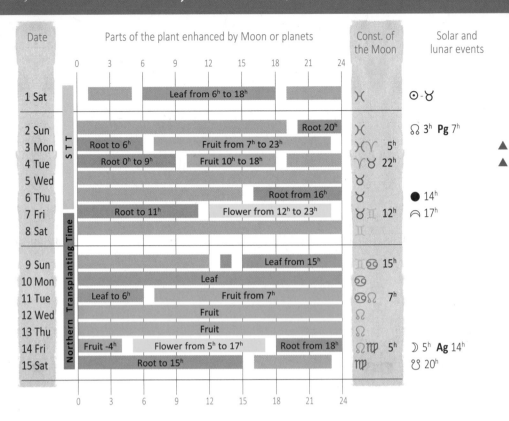

Date	Parts of the plant enhanced by Moon or planets	Const. of the Moon	Solar and lunar events
1 Sat	Leaf from 6ʰ to 18ʰ	♓	☉-♉
2 Sun	Root 20ʰ	♓	☊ 3ʰ **Pg** 7ʰ
3 Mon	Root to 6ʰ — Fruit from 7ʰ to 23ʰ	♓♈ 5ʰ	▲
4 Tue	Root 0ʰ to 9ʰ — Fruit 10ʰ to 18ʰ	♈♉ 22ʰ	▲
5 Wed		♉	
6 Thu	Root from 16ʰ	♉	● 14ʰ
7 Fri	Root to 11ʰ — Flower from 12ʰ to 23ʰ	♉♊ 12ʰ	⌒ 17ʰ
8 Sat		♊	
9 Sun	Leaf from 15ʰ	♊♋ 15ʰ	
10 Mon	Leaf	♋	
11 Tue	Leaf to 6ʰ — Fruit from 7ʰ	♋♌ 7ʰ	
12 Wed	Fruit	♌	
13 Thu	Fruit	♌	
14 Fri	Fruit -4ʰ — Flower from 5ʰ to 17ʰ — Root from 18ʰ	♌♍ 5ʰ	☽ 5ʰ **Ag** 14ʰ
15 Sat	Root to 15ʰ	♍	☋ 20ʰ

(Left margin: STT — Northern Transplanting Time)

Transplanting Time
(time of descending Moon in northern hemisphere)
June 7 19ʰ to June 22 1ʰ

Fruit times
- Tend fruit plants (beans, grains, tomatoes) during these times.
- Sow beans, cucumbers, courgettes (zucchini).

Leaf times 
- Tend leafy plants (like lettuce) during these times.
- Thin and/or transplant (during Transplanting Times) any lettuce, Brussels sprouts, cabbage, kale, etc. that need it.
- Cut aromatic herbs before they bloom.

Flower times
- Tend flowering plants (broccoli, roses) during these times.
- Cut **hay.**
- Pick flowers for teas and dry them in the dark.
- Layer wisteria and trumpet vines.
- Thin or transplant cauliflowers, broccoli.

Root times 
- Tend root plants (carrots, potatoes) during these times.
- Sow winter radishes, swedes (rutabaga), parsnips and carrots for autumn harvesting.

Date	Planetary aspects (**Bold** = visible to naked eye)
1	☾ ☌ ♆ 3ʰ
2	**☾ ☌ ♂ 22ʰ**
3	♃ △ ♇ 0ʰ
4	☿ △ ♇ 6ʰ ☿ ☌ ♃ 10ʰ ☉ ☌ ♀ 16ʰ ☾ ☌ ⚇ 23ʰ
5	**☾ ☌ ♃ 13ʰ ☾ ☌ ☿ 17ʰ**
6	♀ ☍ 3ʰ ☽ ☌ ♀ 14ʰ
7	
8	
9	☿ ☍ 0ʰ ☽ ☍ ♇ 13ʰ
10	
11	
12	
13	☽ ☍ ♄ 20ʰ
14	☉ ☌ ☿ 17ʰ ☽ ☍ ♆ 18ʰ
15	

Planet positions in zodiac

☿ Mercury	♉
♀ Venus	♉
♂ Mars	♓ 8 ♈
♃ Jupiter	♉
♄ Saturn	♒
⚇ Uranus	♉
♆ Neptune	♓
♇ Pluto	♑ (R)

Planet (naked eye) visibility

Evening:
   –

All night:
   –

Morning:
   Mars, Saturn

♓ Pisces	♈ Aries	♉ Taurus	♊ Gemini	♋ Cancer	♌ Leo
♍ Virgo	♎ Libra	♏ Scorpio	♐ Sagittarius	♑ Capricorn	♒ Aquarius

NB: All zodiac symbols refer to astronomical constellations, not astrological signs (see p. 10).

Control pests
(see p. 74 for details)

- **Flies:** burn fly papers at Flower times.
- **Ants** in the house: ash when the Moon is in Leo, June 11 7ʰ to June 14 4ʰ.
- **Slugs:** ash from June 9 15ʰ to June 11 6ʰ.
- **Chitinous insects, wheat weevil, Colorado beetle and varroa:** ash from June 4 22ʰ to June 7 11ʰ.
- **Grasshoppers:** ash from June 7 12ʰ to June 9 14ʰ.

Beekeeping

- Begin **queen bee** rearing (grafting or larval transfer, comb insertion, cell punching) at Flower times.
- Make and sprinkle **varroa ash** between June 4 22ʰ and June 7 11ʰ.
- Possible **swarm time:** May 18 to June 16.

Southern hemisphere

Southern Transplanting Time
May 25 to June 7 15ʰ and June 22 5ʰ to July 4

Notes

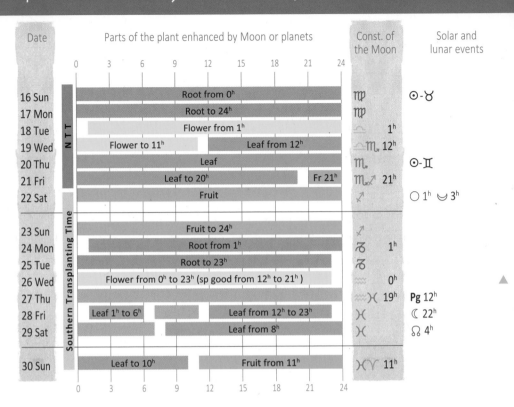

Date	Parts of the plant enhanced by Moon or planets	Const. of the Moon	Solar and lunar events
16 Sun	Root from 0ʰ	♍	☉-♉
17 Mon	Root to 24ʰ	♍	
18 Tue	Flower from 1ʰ	♎ 1ʰ	
19 Wed	Flower to 11ʰ / Leaf from 12ʰ	♎♏ 12ʰ	
20 Thu	Leaf	♏	☉-♊
21 Fri	Leaf to 20ʰ / Fr 21ʰ	♏♐ 21ʰ	
22 Sat	Fruit	♐	○ 1ʰ ☋ 3ʰ
23 Sun	Fruit to 24ʰ	♐	
24 Mon	Root from 1ʰ	♑ 1ʰ	
25 Tue	Root to 23ʰ	♑	
26 Wed	Flower from 0ʰ to 23ʰ (sp good from 12ʰ to 21ʰ)	♒ 0ʰ	
27 Thu		♒♓ 19ʰ	**Pg** 12ʰ
28 Fri	Leaf 1ʰ to 6ʰ / Leaf from 12ʰ to 23ʰ	♓	☽ 22ʰ
29 Sat	Leaf from 8ʰ	♓	☊ 4ʰ
30 Sun	Leaf to 10ʰ / Fruit from 11ʰ	♓♈ 11ʰ	

NTT (Northern Transplanting Time) — Southern Transplanting Time

---

Transplanting Time
(time of descending Moon in northern hemisphere)
June 7 to June 22 1ʰ

Fruit times

- Tend fruit plants (beans, grains, tomatoes) during these times.
- Harvest tomatoes.
- Sow courgettes (zucchini).
- Lightly prune fruit trees and shrubs.

Leaf times

- Tend leafy plants (like lettuce) during these times.
- Cut aromatic herbs before they bloom.
- Mow lawns if you want to encourage vigorous growth of the grass.

Flower times

- Tend flowering plants (broccoli, roses) during these times.
- Cut **hay.**

Root times

- Tend root plants (carrots, potatoes) during these times.
- Harvest early potatoes as needed.
- Harvest onions, garlic, shallots, and dry before storing.

Beekeeping
Begin **queen bee** rearing (grafting or larval transfer, comb insertion, cell punching) at Flower times.

Date	Planetary aspects (**Bold** = visible to naked eye)
16	
17	☿ ☌ ♀ 13ʰ ☽ ☍ ♂ 19ʰ
18	
19	☽ ☍ ⊕ 7ʰ
20	☽ ☍ ♃ 3ʰ
21	
22	☾ ☍ ♀ 10ʰ ☾ ☍ ☿ 19ʰ
23	
24	☾ ☌ ♇ 6ʰ
25	
26	☿ △ ♄ 18ʰ
27	☾ • ♄ 15ʰ
28	☾ • ♆ 9ʰ
29	
30	

Planet positions in zodiac

☿	Mercury	♉ 17 ♊
♀	Venus	♉ 17 ♊
♂	Mars	♈
♃	Jupiter	♉
♄	Saturn	♒ (29 R)
⛢	Uranus	♉
♆	Neptune	♓
♇	Pluto	♑ (R)

Planet (naked eye) visibility

Evening:
–

All night: –

Morning:
Mars,
Jupiter (from June 16),
Saturn

♓ Pisces	♈ Aries	♉ Taurus	♊ Gemini
♋ Cancer	♌ Leo		
♍ Virgo	♎ Libra	♏ Scorpio	♐ Sagittarius
♑ Capricorn	♒ Aquarius		

NB: All zodiac symbols refer to astronomical constellations, not astrological signs (see p. 10).

Control pests
(see p. 74 for details)

- **Flies:** burn fly papers at Flower times.
- **Mole crickets:** ash from June 19 12ʰ to June 21 20ʰ.
- **Grasshoppers:** ash from June 26 0ʰ to June 27 18ʰ.

Southern hemisphere

Southern Transplanting Time
June 22 5ʰ to July 4

Biodynamic preparations

Look for the places where **valerian** is growing to save time searching for it when it comes to harvesting in July and August.

Tip

Want to know more about biodynamic preparations?
- See 'Biodynamic preparations', p. 73.

Notes

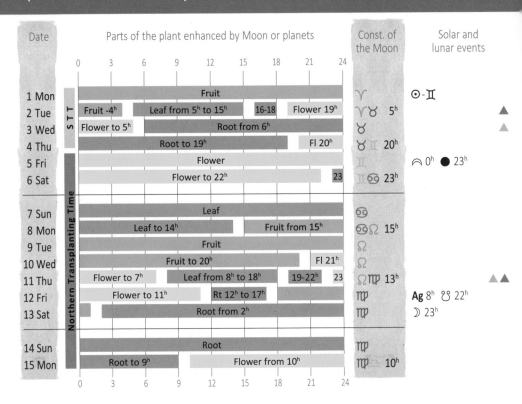

Date	Parts of the plant enhanced by Moon or planets	Const. of the Moon	Solar and lunar events
1 Mon	Fruit	♈	☉-♊
2 Tue	Fruit -4ʰ · Leaf from 5ʰ to 15ʰ · 16-18 · Flower 19ʰ	♈ ♉ 5ʰ	▲
3 Wed	Flower to 5ʰ · Root from 6ʰ	♉	▲
4 Thu	Root to 19ʰ · Fl 20ʰ	♉ ♊ 20ʰ	
5 Fri	Flower	♊	⌒ 0ʰ ● 23ʰ
6 Sat	Flower to 22ʰ · 23	♊ ♋ 23ʰ	
7 Sun	Leaf	♋	
8 Mon	Leaf to 14ʰ · Fruit from 15ʰ	♋ ♌ 15ʰ	
9 Tue	Fruit	♌	
10 Wed	Fruit to 20ʰ · Fl 21ʰ	♌	
11 Thu	Flower to 7ʰ · Leaf from 8ʰ to 18ʰ · 19-22ʰ · 23	♌ ♍ 13ʰ	▲▲
12 Fri	Flower to 11ʰ · Rt 12ʰ to 17ʰ	♍	Ag 8ʰ ☊ 22ʰ
13 Sat	Root from 2ʰ	♍	☽ 23ʰ
14 Sun	Root	♍	
15 Mon	Root to 9ʰ · Flower from 10ʰ	♍ 10ʰ	

(Left margin: S T T · Northern Transplanting Time)

Transplanting Time
(time of descending Moon in northern hemisphere)
July 5 2ʰ to July 19 9ʰ

Leaf times

- Tend leafy plants (like lettuce) during these times.
- Harvest **seeds of leaf plants** to be used for seed.
- Spray leaf plants and the soil with horn silica early in the morning.

Root times

- Tend root plants (carrots, potatoes) during these times.
- Harvest **seeds of root plants** to be used for seed.

Fruit times

- Tend fruit plants (beans, grains, tomatoes) during these times.
- Harvest **seeds of fruit plants** and **grain** to be used for seed.
- Sow climbing and runner (pole) beans.
- Prune tomato suckers or side shoots.

Flower times

- Tend flowering plants (broccoli, roses) during these times.
- Harvest **seeds of flower plants** to be used for seed.
- Cut **late hay.**
- Sow biennials such as pansies, and perennials like hyssop, columbine, etc.

Date	Planetary aspects (**Bold** = visible to naked eye)
1	☾☌♂ 18ʰ
2	☾☌⚷ 9ʰ ☿△♆ 12ʰ
3	♀△♄ 2ʰ ☿☍♇ 7ʰ **☾☌♃ 7ʰ**
4	
5	
6	☽☌♀ 16ʰ
7	☽☍♇ 6ʰ ☽☌☿ 20ʰ
8	
9	
10	
11	☉△♄ 3ʰ ☽☍♄ 4ʰ ♀△♆ 15ʰ
12	☽☍♆ 2ʰ ♀☍♇ 14ʰ
13	
14	
15	♂☌⚷ 14ʰ

Planet positions in zodiac

☿	Mercury	♊	1 ♋
			14 ♌
♀	Venus	♊	9 ♋
♂	Mars	♈	11 ♉
♃	Jupiter	♉	
♄	Saturn	♒	(R)
⚷	Uranus	♉	
♆	Neptune	♓	(2 R)
♇	Pluto	♑	(R)

Planet (naked eye) visibility

Evening:
Venus (from July 10)

All night:
–

Morning:
Mars, Jupiter, Saturn

♓ Pisces	♈ Aries	♉ Taurus	♊ Gemini	♋ Cancer	♌ Leo
♍ Virgo	♎ Libra	♏ Scorpio	♐ Sagittarius	♑ Capricorn	♒ Aquarius

NB: All zodiac symbols refer to astronomical constellations, not astrological signs (see p. 10).

Control pests
(see p. 74 for details)

- **Flies:** burn fly papers at Flower times.
- **Slugs:** ash from July 6 23ʰ to July 8 14ʰ. Spray leaf plants and the soil with horn silica early in the morning during Leaf times.
- **Grasshoppers:** ash from July 4 20ʰ to July 6 22ʰ.
- **Ants** in the house: ash when the Moon is in Leo, July 8 15ʰ to July 11 12ʰ.

Biodynamic preparations

Pick **valerian** flowers at Flower times early in the morning while there is still plenty of night-time moisture around. The juice should be pressed out immediately without adding any water or leaving the plants in water. Juice to which water has been added will not keep long.

Southern hemisphere

Southern Transplanting Time
June 22 to July 4 22ʰ and July 19 13ʰ to Aug 1 4ʰ

Maria Thun's tree log preparations

- Cut **larch** logs, fill with dried **camomile** and put them into the ground between July 2 20ʰ and July 3 13ʰ.
- Cut **birch** logs, fill with dried **yarrow** and put them into the ground on July 12 between 3ʰ and 17ʰ.

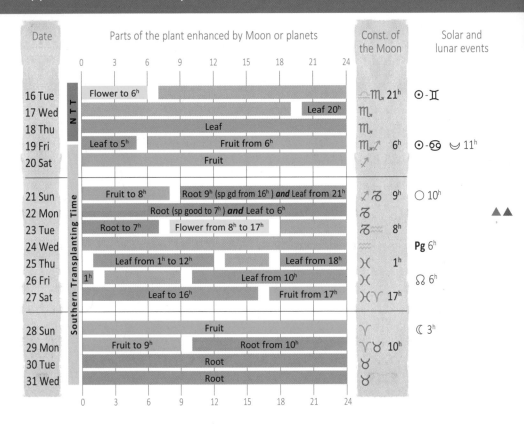

Date	Parts of the plant enhanced by Moon or planets	Const. of the Moon	Solar and lunar events
16 Tue	Flower to 6ʰ	♎ ♏ 21ʰ	☉-♊
17 Wed	Leaf 20ʰ	♏	
18 Thu	Leaf	♏	
19 Fri	Leaf to 5ʰ / Fruit from 6ʰ	♏ ♐ 6ʰ	☉-♋ ☽ 11ʰ
20 Sat	Fruit	♐	
21 Sun	Fruit to 8ʰ / Root 9ʰ (sp gd from 16ʰ) *and* Leaf from 21ʰ	♐ ♑ 9ʰ	○ 10ʰ
22 Mon	Root (sp good to 7ʰ) *and* Leaf to 6ʰ	♑	
23 Tue	Root to 7ʰ / Flower from 8ʰ to 17ʰ	♑ ♒ 8ʰ	
24 Wed		♒	Pg 6ʰ
25 Thu	Leaf from 1ʰ to 12ʰ / Leaf from 18ʰ	♓ 1ʰ	
26 Fri	1ʰ / Leaf from 10ʰ	♓	♌ 6ʰ
27 Sat	Leaf to 16ʰ / Fruit from 17ʰ	♓ ♈ 17ʰ	
28 Sun	Fruit	♈	☾ 3ʰ
29 Mon	Fruit to 9ʰ / Root from 10ʰ	♈ ♉ 10ʰ	
30 Tue	Root	♉	
31 Wed	Root	♉	

N T T (16–20)

Southern Transplanting Time (21–31)

▲▲ (22 Mon)

Transplanting Time

(time of descending Moon in northern hemisphere)

July 5 to July 19 9ʰ

Fruit times

- Tend fruit plants (beans, grains, tomatoes) during these times.
- Harvest **seeds of fruit plants** and **grain** to be used for seed.
- Cut raspberry canes that have finished bearing fruit.

Leaf times

- Tend leafy plants (like lettuce) during these times.
- Harvest **seeds of leaf plants** to be used for seed.
- Spray leaf plants and the soil with horn silica early in the morning.

Flower times

- Tend flowering plants (broccoli, roses) during these times.
- Harvest **seeds of flower plants** to be used for seed.
- Cut **late hay.**
- Plant autumn flowering bulbs.
- Graft rosehips.

Root times

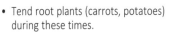

- Tend root plants (carrots, potatoes) during these times.
- Harvest **seeds of root plants** to be used for seed.

Date	Planetary aspects (**Bold** = visible to naked eye)
16	☽☌♅ 19ʰ ☽☌♂ 20ʰ
17	☿♉ 7ʰ ☽☌♃ 23ʰ
18	
19	
20	
21	☾☌♇ 13ʰ
22	☉△♆ 3ʰ ♂△♇ 4ʰ ☾☍♀ 10ʰ
23	☉☍♇ 5ʰ ☾☍☿ 10ʰ
24	☾●♄ 21ʰ
25	☾●♆ 15ʰ
26	
27	
28	
29	☾☌♅ 16ʰ
30	☾☌♂ 9ʰ ☾☌♃ 23ʰ
31	

Planet positions in zodiac

☿	Mercury	♌	
♀	Venus	♋	26 ♌
♂	Mars	♉	
♃	Jupiter	♉	
♄	Saturn	♒	(R)
♅	Uranus	♉	
♆	Neptune	♓	(R)
♇	Pluto	♑	(R)

Planet (naked eye) visibility

Evening:
    Venus

All night:
    –

Morning:
    Mars, Jupiter, Saturn

♓ Pisces	♈ Aries	♉ Taurus	♊ Gemini	♋ Cancer	♌ Leo
♍ Virgo	♎ Libra	♏ Scorpio	♐ Sagittarius	♑ Capricorn	♒ Aquarius

---

Control pests
(see p. 74 for details)

- **Flies:** burn fly papers at Flower times.
- **Grasshoppers:** ash from July 23 8ʰ to July 24 24ʰ.

Biodynamic preparations

Pick **Valerian** flowers at Flower times early in the morning while there is still plenty of night-time moisture around. The juice should be pressed out immediately without adding any water or leaving the plants in water. Juice to which water has been added will not keep long.

Southern hemisphere

Southern Transplanting Time
July 19 13ʰ to Aug 1 4ʰ

Maria Thun's tree log preparations

- Cut **maple** logs, fill with dried **dandelion** and put them into the ground between July 22 18ʰ and July 23 11ʰ.

Tip

Want to know more about biodynamic preparations?
- See 'Biodynamic preparations', p. 73.

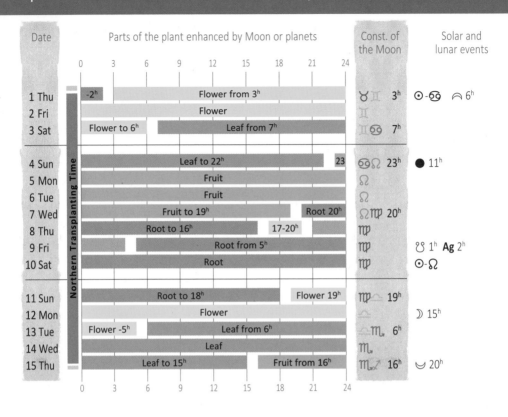

Date	Parts of the plant enhanced by Moon or planets	Const. of the Moon	Solar and lunar events
1 Thu	-2ʰ Flower from 3ʰ	♉♊ 3ʰ	☉-♋ ⌢ 6ʰ
2 Fri	Flower	♊	
3 Sat	Flower to 6ʰ Leaf from 7ʰ	♊♋ 7ʰ	
4 Sun	Leaf to 22ʰ 23	♋♌ 23ʰ	● 11ʰ
5 Mon	Fruit	♌	
6 Tue	Fruit	♌	
7 Wed	Fruit to 19ʰ Root 20ʰ	♌♍ 20ʰ	
8 Thu	Root to 16ʰ 17-20ʰ	♍	
9 Fri	Root from 5ʰ	♍	☋ 1ʰ **Ag** 2ʰ
10 Sat	Root	♍	☉-♌
11 Sun	Root to 18ʰ Flower 19ʰ	♍⌢ 19ʰ	
12 Mon	Flower	⌢	☽ 15ʰ
13 Tue	Flower -5ʰ Leaf from 6ʰ	⌢♏ 6ʰ	
14 Wed	Leaf	♏	
15 Thu	Leaf to 15ʰ Fruit from 16ʰ	♏♐ 16ʰ	⌣ 20ʰ

Northern Transplanting Time

Transplanting Time
(time of descending Moon in northern hemisphere)
Aug 1 8ʰ to Aug 15 18ʰ and Aug 28 13ʰ to Sep 12

Leaf times

- Tend leafy plants (like lettuce) during these times.
- Harvest **seeds of leaf plants** to be used for seed.
- Sow weather hardy lamb's lettuce and cabbage.

Root times

- Tend root plants (carrots, potatoes).
- Harvest **seeds of root plants** to be used for seed.
- Harvest carrots, onions, potatoes.

Fruit times

- Tend fruit plants (beans, grains, tomatoes) during these times.
- Harvest **seeds of fruit plants** and **grain** to be used for seed.
- Immediately after harvest, sow catch crops like lupins, phacelia, mustard or wild flax.
- After the harvest prune fruit trees.

Flower times
- Tend flowering plants (broccoli, roses) during these times.
- Harvest **seeds of flower plants** to be used for seed.
- Prune roses.

Date	Planetary aspects (**Bold** = visible to naked eye)
1	
2	
3	☾ ☌ ♇ 12ʰ
4	
5	☽ ☌ ♀ 23ʰ
6	☽ ☌ ☿ 5ʰ
7	☽ ☍ ♄ 10ʰ
8	☿ ☌ ♀ 3ʰ ☽ ☍ ♅ 9ʰ
9	
10	
11	
12	
13	☽ ☍ ♁ 4ʰ
14	♂ ☌ ♃ 15ʰ ☽ ☌ ♃ 18ʰ ☽ ☌ ♂ 18ʰ
15	

Planet positions in zodiac

☿	Mercury	♌	(5 R)
♀	Venus	♌	
♂	Mars	♉	
♃	Jupiter	♉	
♄	Saturn	♒	(R)
♅	Uranus	♉	
♆	Neptune	♓	(R)
♇	Pluto	♑	(R)

Planet (naked eye) visibility

Evening:
   Venus

All night:
   –

Morning:
   Mars, Jupiter, Saturn

♓ Pisces	♈ Aries	♉ Taurus	♊ Gemini	♋ Cancer	♌ Leo
♍ Virgo	♎ Libra	♏ Scorpio	♐ Sagittarius	♑ Capricorn	♒ Aquarius

NB: All zodiac symbols refer to astronomical constellations, not astrological signs (see p. 10).

Control pests
(see p. 74 for details)

- **Flies:** burn fly papers at Flower times.
- **Slugs:** ash from Aug 3 7ʰ to Aug 4 22ʰ.
- **Ants** in the house: ash when the Moon is in Leo, Aug 4 23ʰ to Aug 7 19ʰ.

Biodynamic preparations

Cut **yarrow** in the mornings at Fruit times after Aug 15. The blossoms should show some seed formation.

Southern hemisphere

Southern Transplanting Time
July 19 to Aug 1 4ʰ and Aug 15 22ʰ to Aug 28 9ʰ

Notes

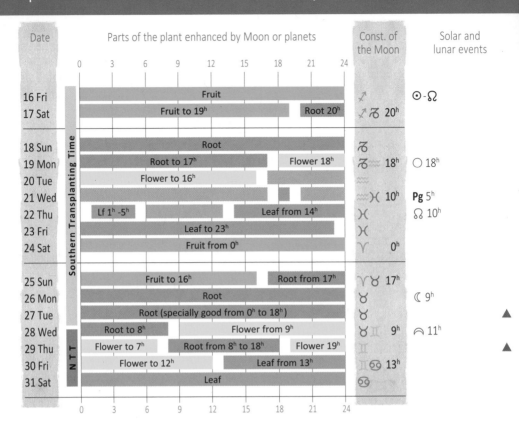

Chart: Parts of the plant enhanced by Moon or planets (Southern Transplanting Time)

Date	Parts of the plant enhanced by Moon or planets	Const. of the Moon	Solar and lunar events
16 Fri	Fruit	♐	☉-♌
17 Sat	Fruit to 19ʰ · Root 20ʰ	♐ ♑ 20ʰ	
18 Sun	Root	♑	
19 Mon	Root to 17ʰ · Flower 18ʰ	♑ ♒ 18ʰ	○ 18ʰ
20 Tue	Flower to 16ʰ	♒	
21 Wed		♒ ♓ 10ʰ	Pg 5ʰ
22 Thu	Lf 1ʰ-5ʰ · Leaf from 14ʰ	♓	☊ 10ʰ
23 Fri	Leaf to 23ʰ	♓	
24 Sat	Fruit from 0ʰ	♈ 0ʰ	
25 Sun	Fruit to 16ʰ · Root from 17ʰ	♈ ♉ 17ʰ	
26 Mon	Root	♉	☾ 9ʰ
27 Tue	Root (specially good from 0ʰ to 18ʰ)	♉	⌒ 11ʰ
28 Wed	Root to 8ʰ · Flower from 9ʰ	♉ ♊ 9ʰ	
29 Thu	Flower to 7ʰ · Root from 8ʰ to 18ʰ · Flower 19ʰ	♊	
30 Fri	Flower to 12ʰ · Leaf from 13ʰ	♊ ♋ 13ʰ	
31 Sat	Leaf	♋	

(Southern Transplanting Time indicated left of chart; NTT marked Aug 28–31)

Transplanting Time
(time of descending Moon in northern hemisphere)
Aug 28 13ʰ to Sep 12

Fruit times

- Tend fruit plants (beans, grains, tomatoes) during these times.
- Harvest **seeds of fruit plants** and **grain** to be used for seed.
- Immediately after harvest, sow catch crops like lupins, phacelia, mustard or wild flax.

Leaf times

- Tend leafy plants (like lettuce) during these times.
- Harvest **seeds of leaf plants** to be used for seed.
- Mow lawns if you want to encourage vigorous growth of the grass.

Flower times

- Tend flowering plants (broccoli, roses) during these times.
- Harvest **seeds of flower plants** to be used for seed.
- Sow hardy annuals for early bloom next spring.
- Graft rosehips.

Root times

- Tend root plants (carrots, potatoes) during these times.
- Harvest **seeds of leaf plants** to be used for seed.

Date	Planetary aspects
	(**Bold** = visible to naked eye)

Planet positions in zodiac

☿ Mercury	♌ (R 28 D)
♀ Venus	♌ 24 ♍
♂ Mars	♉
♃ Jupiter	♉
♄ Saturn	♒ (R)
♅ Uranus	♉
♆ Neptune	♓ (R)
♇ Pluto	♑ (R)

Date	Aspects
16	
17	☽ ☌ ♇ 22ʰ
18	
19	☉ ☌ ☿ 2ʰ ♀ ☍ ♄ 9ʰ ☽ ☍ ☿ 17ʰ
20	
21	**☾ ☌ ♄ 3ʰ ☾ ☍ ♀ 7ʰ ☾ ☌ ♆ 22ʰ**
22	
23	
24	
25	**☾ ☌ ♅ 22ʰ**
26	
27	♀ △ ♅ 7ʰ **☾ ☌ ♃ 12ʰ**
28	**☾ ☌ ♂ 0ʰ** ♀ ☍ ♆ 21ʰ
29	♀ △ ♇ 15ʰ
30	**☾ ☍ ♇ 17ʰ**
31	

Planet (naked eye) visibility

Evening:
Venus

All night:
–

Morning:
Mercury (from Aug 29),
Mars, Jupiter, Saturn

♓ Pisces	♈ Aries	♉ Taurus	♊ Gemini	♋ Cancer	♌ Leo
♍ Virgo	♎ Libra	♏ Scorpio	♐ Sagittarius	♑ Capricorn	♒ Aquarius

Control pests
(see p. 74 for details)

- **Slugs:** ash from Aug 30 13ʰ to Sep 1 5ʰ.
- **Flies:** burn fly papers at Flower times.

Southern hemisphere

Southern Transplanting Time
Aug 15 to Aug 28 9ʰ

Biodynamic preparations

Cut **yarrow** in the mornings at Fruit times after Aug 15. The blossoms should show some seed formation.

Maria Thun's tree log preparations

- Cut **birch** logs, fill with dried **yarrow** and put them into the ground between Aug 18 22ʰ and Aug 19 15ʰ or between Aug 28 10ʰ and Aug 29 3ʰ.

Notes

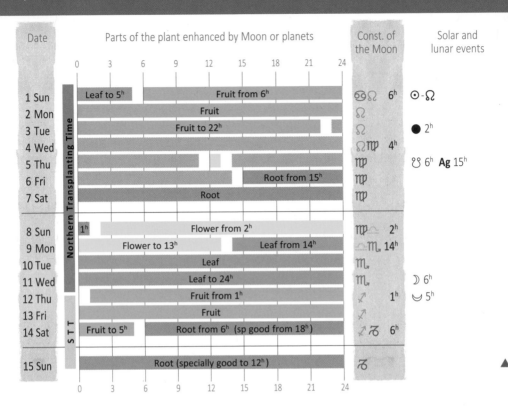

Date	Parts of the plant enhanced by Moon or planets	Const. of the Moon	Solar and lunar events
1 Sun	Leaf to 5ʰ / Fruit from 6ʰ	♋♌ 6ʰ	☉-♌
2 Mon	Fruit	♌	
3 Tue	Fruit to 22ʰ	♌	● 2ʰ
4 Wed		♌♍ 4ʰ	
5 Thu		♍	☊ 6ʰ **Ag** 15ʰ
6 Fri	Root from 15ʰ	♍	
7 Sat	Root	♍	
8 Sun	1ʰ Flower from 2ʰ	♍♎ 2ʰ	
9 Mon	Flower to 13ʰ / Leaf from 14ʰ	♎♏ 14ʰ	
10 Tue	Leaf	♏	
11 Wed	Leaf to 24ʰ	♏	☽ 6ʰ
12 Thu	Fruit from 1ʰ	♐ 1ʰ	‿ 5ʰ
13 Fri	Fruit	♐	
14 Sat	Fruit to 5ʰ / Root from 6ʰ (sp good from 18ʰ)	♐♑ 6ʰ	
15 Sun	Root (specially good to 12ʰ)	♑	▲

Northern Transplanting Time / STT

Transplanting Time
(time of descending Moon in northern hemisphere)
Aug 28 to Sep 12 3ʰ and Sep 24 19ʰ to Oct 9

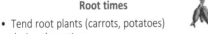

Leaf times

- Tend leafy plants (like lettuce) during these times.

Root times

- Tend root plants (carrots, potatoes) during these times.
- The harvest of **root crops** is always best undertaken at Root times. Storage trials of onions, carrots, beetroots (beets) and potatoes have demonstrated this time and again.

Fruit times

- Tend fruit plants (beans, grains, tomatoes) during these times.
- Good times to **harvest fruit** are when the Moon is in Sagittarius (Sep 12 1ʰ to Sep 14 5ʰ) or Aries, or other Fruit times, always avoiding unfavourable times.
- Good times for **sowing winter grain** are when the Moon is in Leo (Sep 1 6ʰ to Sep 3 22ʰ) or Sagittarius (Sep 12 1ʰ to Sep 14 5ʰ) avoiding unfavourable times, and at other Fruit times.
- **Rye** can, if necessary, also be sown at Root times with all subsequent cultivations being carried out at Fruit times.

Flower times

- Tend flowering plants (broccoli, roses) during these times.
- During Transplanting Time transplant annuals and bienniels sown earlier.

Date	Planetary aspects (**Bold** = visible to naked eye)
1	☾ ☌ ☿ 13ʰ
2	
3	☽ ☍ ♄ 13ʰ
4	☽ ☍ ♆ 14ʰ ☿ ♌ 23ʰ
5	☽ • ♀ 9ʰ
6	♂ ♌ 2ʰ
7	
8	☉ ☍ ♄ 4ʰ
9	☽ ☍ ⚨ 12ʰ
10	
11	☽ ☍ ♃ 8ʰ
12	☽ ☍ ♂ 11ʰ
13	
14	☽ ☌ ♇ 8ʰ
15	♀ △ ♃ 6ʰ

Planet positions in zodiac

☿	Mercury	♌
♀	Venus	♍
♂	Mars	♉ 4 ♊
♃	Jupiter	♉
♄	Saturn	♒ (R)
⚨	Uranus	♉ (1 R)
♆	Neptune	♓ (R)
♇	Pluto	♑ (R)

Planet (naked eye) visibility

Evening:
Venus

All night:
Saturn

Morning:
Mercury, Mars, Jupiter

♓ Pisces	♈ Aries	♉ Taurus	♊ Gemini
♋ Cancer	♌ Leo	♍ Virgo	♎ Libra
♏ Scorpio	♐ Sagittarius	♑ Capricorn	♒ Aquarius

NB: All zodiac symbols refer to astronomical constellations, not astrological signs (see p. 10).

Control pests
(see p. 74 for details)

- **Flies:** burn fly papers at Flower times.
- **Slugs:** ash from Aug 30 13ʰ to Sep 1 5ʰ.

Biodynamic preparations

Cut **yarrow** in the mornings at Fruit times before Sep 16. The blossoms should show some seed formation.

Maria Thun's tree log preparations

- Cut **maple** logs, fill with dried **dandelion** and put them into the ground between Sep 7 17ʰ and Sep 8 10ʰ.

Southern hemisphere

Southern Transplanting Time
Sep 12 7ʰ to Sep 24 15ʰ

Notes

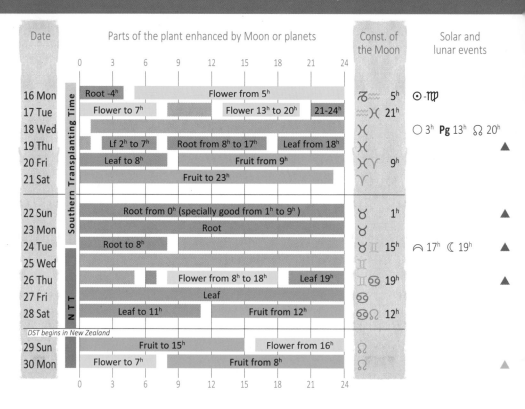

Date	Parts of the plant enhanced by Moon or planets	Const. of the Moon	Solar and lunar events
16 Mon	Root -4ʰ Flower from 5ʰ	♑ ♒ 5ʰ	☉-♍
17 Tue	Flower to 7ʰ Flower 13ʰ to 20ʰ 21-24ʰ	♒ ♓ 21ʰ	
18 Wed		♓	○ 3ʰ **Pg** 13ʰ ☊ 20ʰ
19 Thu	Lf 2ʰ to 7ʰ Root from 8ʰ to 17ʰ Leaf from 18ʰ	♓	▲
20 Fri	Leaf to 8ʰ Fruit from 9ʰ	♓ ♈ 9ʰ	
21 Sat	Fruit to 23ʰ	♈	
22 Sun	Root from 0ʰ (specially good from 1ʰ to 9ʰ)	♉ 1ʰ	▲
23 Mon	Root	♉	
24 Tue	Root to 8ʰ	♉ ♊ 15ʰ	⌒ 17ʰ ☾ 19ʰ ▲
25 Wed		♊	
26 Thu	Flower from 8ʰ to 18ʰ Leaf 19ʰ	♊ ♋ 19ʰ	▲
27 Fri	Leaf	♋	
28 Sat	Leaf to 11ʰ Fruit from 12ʰ	♋ ♌ 12ʰ	
29 Sun	Fruit to 15ʰ Flower from 16ʰ	♌	▲
30 Mon	Flower to 7ʰ Fruit from 8ʰ	♌	▲

Southern Transplanting Time (left margin, 16 Mon – 24 Tue)

NTT (left margin, 27 Fri – 28 Sat)

DST begins in New Zealand

Transplanting Time
(time of descending Moon in northern hemisphere)
Sep 24 19ʰ to Oct 9

Leaf times

- Tend leafy plants (like lettuce) during these times.
- Plant conifer and evergreen shrubs.

Root times

- Tend root plants (carrots, potatoes) during these times.
- The harvest of **root crops** is always best undertaken at Root times. Storage trials of onions, carrots, beetroots (beets) and potatoes have demonstrated this time and again.
- Sow radishes in a cold frame.

Fruit times

- Tend fruit plants (beans, grains, tomatoes) during these times.
- Good times to **harvest fruit** are when the Moon is in Sagittarius or Aries (Sep 20 9ʰ to Sep 21 23ʰ), or other Fruit times, always avoiding unfavourable times.
- Good times for **sowing winter grain** are when the Moon is in Leo (Sep 28 12ʰ to Oct 1 9ʰ) or Sagittarius.
- **Rye** can, if necessary, also be sown at Root times with all subsequent cultivations being carried out at Fruit times.

Flower times

- Tend flowering plants (broccoli, roses) during these times.
- During Transplanting Time transplant annuals and bienniels sown earlier.

Date	Planetary aspects (**Bold** = visible to naked eye)
16	
17	☽☌☿ 7ʰ ☽•♄ 10ʰ
18	☾•♆ 7ʰ ☿☍♄ 9ʰ
19	☉△♁ 14ʰ
20	☾☍♀ 3ʰ
21	☉☍♆ 0ʰ
22	☾☌♁ 5ʰ ☉△♇ 6ʰ
23	☾☌♃ 23ʰ
24	☿△♁ 17ʰ
25	☿☍♆ 11ʰ ☾☌♂ 13ʰ ♀☊ 17ʰ
26	☿△♇ 4ʰ ☾☍♇ 22ʰ
27	
28	
29	
30	♂△♄ 4ʰ ☾☍♄ 15ʰ ☉☌☿ 21ʰ

Planet positions in zodiac

☿ Mercury	♌ 22 ♍	
♀ Venus	♍	
♂ Mars	♊	
♃ Jupiter	♉	
♄ Saturn	♒	(R)
♁ Uranus	♉	(R)
♆ Neptune	♓	(R)
♇ Pluto	♑	(R)

Planet (naked eye) visibility

Evening:
Venus

All night:
Saturn

Morning:
Mercury (to Sep 20),
Mars, Jupiter

♓ Pisces	♈ Aries	♉ Taurus	♊ Gemini	♋ Cancer	♌ Leo
♍ Virgo	♎ Libra	♏ Scorpio	♐ Sagittarius	♑ Capricorn	♒ Aquarius

NB: All zodiac symbols refer to astronomical constellations, not astrological signs (see p. 10).

Control pests
(see p. 74 for details)

- **Flies:** burn fly papers at Flower times.
- **Slugs:** ash from Sep 26 19ʰ to Sep 28 11ʰ.

Southern hemisphere

Southern Transplanting Time
Sep 12 to Sep 24 15ʰ

Maria Thun's tree log preparations

- Cut **maple** logs, fill with dried **dandelion** and put them into the ground between Sep 20 13ʰ and Sep 21 6ʰ.

Notes

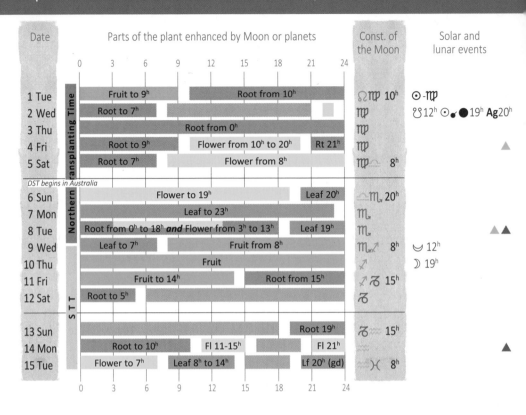

Date	Parts of the plant enhanced by Moon or planets	Const. of the Moon	Solar and lunar events

(Hour scale across top: 0 3 6 9 12 15 18 21 24)

Date	Plant parts	Const. of the Moon	Solar and lunar events
1 Tue	Fruit to 9ʰ — Root from 10ʰ	♌♍ 10ʰ	☉-♍
2 Wed	Root to 7ʰ	♍	☊12ʰ ☉☌● 19ʰ Ag20ʰ
3 Thu	Root from 0ʰ	♍	
4 Fri	Root to 9ʰ — Flower from 10ʰ to 20ʰ — Rt 21ʰ	♍	▲
5 Sat	Root to 7ʰ — Flower from 8ʰ	♍♎ 8ʰ	

DST begins in Australia

Date	Plant parts	Const. of the Moon	Solar and lunar events
6 Sun	Flower to 19ʰ — Leaf 20ʰ	♎♏ 20ʰ	
7 Mon	Leaf to 23ʰ	♏	
8 Tue	Root from 0ʰ to 18ʰ **and** Flower from 3ʰ to 13ʰ — Leaf 19ʰ	♏	▲▲
9 Wed	Leaf to 7ʰ — Fruit from 8ʰ	♏♐ 8ʰ	☌ 12ʰ
10 Thu	Fruit	♐	☽ 19ʰ
11 Fri	Fruit to 14ʰ — Root from 15ʰ	♐♑ 15ʰ	
12 Sat	Root to 5ʰ	♑	

(S T T marking)

Date	Plant parts	Const. of the Moon	Solar and lunar events
13 Sun	Root 19ʰ	♑♒ 15ʰ	
14 Mon	Root to 10ʰ — Fl 11–15ʰ — Fl 21ʰ	♒	▲
15 Tue	Flower to 7ʰ — Leaf 8ʰ to 14ʰ — Lf 20ʰ (gd)	♓ 8ʰ	

(Hour scale across bottom: 0 3 6 9 12 15 18 21 24)

(Left margin: Northern Transplanting Time)

Transplanting Time
(time of descending Moon in northern hemisphere)
Sep 24 to Oct 9 10ʰ and Oct 22 3ʰ to Nov 5

Fruit times

- Tend fruit plants (beans, grains, tomatoes) during these times.
- **Store fruit** at any Fruit or Flower time outside Transplanting Time.
- Harvest squash and any ripe fruit.

Leaf times

- Tend leafy plants (like lettuce) during these times.
- Harvest **seeds of leaf plants.**
- Sow spinach, winter lettuce, lamb's lettuce (in a greenhouse if necessary).

Flower times

- Tend flowering plants (broccoli, roses) during these times.
- Harvest **seeds of flower plants.**
- Sow annual sweet peas in a greenhouse.

Root times

- Tend root plants (carrots, potatoes) during these times.
- Harvest **seeds of root plants.**
- In sunny regions sow radishes.

Date	Planetary aspects (**Bold** = visible to naked eye)
1	☾ ☌ ♆ 19ʰ
2	☽ ☌ ☿ 22ʰ
3	
4	♀ △ ♄ 17ʰ
5	☽ ☌ ♀ 18ʰ
6	☽ ☍ ♅ 17ʰ
7	
8	♀ △ ♂ 10ʰ ☿ △ ♃ 12ʰ ☽ ☍ ♃ 17ʰ
9	
10	☽ ☍ ♂ 22ʰ
11	☽ ☌ ♇ 16ʰ
12	
13	☿ ☊ 6ʰ
14	☉ △ ♃ 4ʰ ☽ ☌ ♄ 18ʰ ♀ ☍ ♅ 22ʰ
15	☽ ☌ ♆ 17ʰ

Planet positions in zodiac

☿ Mercury	♍
♀ Venus	♍ 1 ♎ 15 ♏
♂ Mars	♊
♃ Jupiter	♉ (9 R)
♄ Saturn	♒ (R)
♅ Uranus	♉ (R)
♆ Neptune	♓ (R)
♇ Pluto	♑ (R 12 D)

Planet (naked eye) visibility

Evening:
 Venus

All night:
 Jupiter, Saturn

Morning:
 Mars

| ♓ Pisces | ♈ Aries | ♉ Taurus | ♊ Gemini | ♋ Cancer | ♌ Leo |
| ♍ Virgo | ♎ Libra | ♏ Scorpio | ♐ Sagittarius | ♑ Capricorn | ♒ Aquarius |

NB: All zodiac symbols refer to astronomical constellations, not astrological signs (see p. 10).

Control pests
(see p. 74 for details)
- **Flies:** burn fly papers at Flower times.

Southern hemisphere
Southern Transplanting Time
Oct 9 14ʰ to Oct 21 23ʰ

Treating cleared ground
All **cleared ground** should be treated with compost, sprayed with barrel preparation and ploughed ready for winter.

Notes

Date	Parts of the plant enhanced by Moon or planets	Const. of the Moon	Solar and lunar events

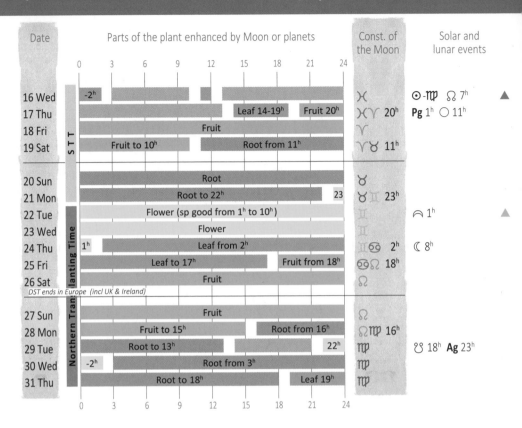

Chart (hours 0–24):

Date	Parts of the plant enhanced by Moon or planets	Const. of the Moon	Solar and lunar events
16 Wed	-2ʰ	♓	☉-♍ ☍ 7ʰ ▲
17 Thu	Leaf 14-19ʰ Fruit 20ʰ	♓♈ 20ʰ	Pg 1ʰ ○ 11ʰ
18 Fri	Fruit	♈	
19 Sat	Fruit to 10ʰ Root from 11ʰ	♈♉ 11ʰ	
20 Sun	Root	♉	
21 Mon	Root to 22ʰ 23	♉♊ 23ʰ	
22 Tue	Flower (sp good from 1ʰ to 10ʰ)	♊	⌢ 1ʰ ▲
23 Wed	Flower	♊	
24 Thu	1ʰ Leaf from 2ʰ	♊♋ 2ʰ	☾ 8ʰ
25 Fri	Leaf to 17ʰ Fruit from 18ʰ	♋♌ 18ʰ	
26 Sat	Fruit	♌	
27 Sun	Fruit	♌	
28 Mon	Fruit to 15ʰ Root from 16ʰ	♌♍ 16ʰ	
29 Tue	Root to 13ʰ 22ʰ	♍	♉ 18ʰ **Ag** 23ʰ
30 Wed	-2ʰ Root from 3ʰ	♍	
31 Thu	Root to 18ʰ Leaf 19ʰ	♍	

STT

Northern Transplanting Time

DST ends in Europe (incl UK & Ireland) (between 26 Sat and 27 Sun)

Transplanting Time
(time of descending Moon in northern hemisphere)
Oct 22 3ʰ to Nov 5

Fruit times

- Tend fruit plants (beans, grains, tomatoes) during these times.
- **Store fruit** at any Fruit or Flower time outside Transplanting Time.
- Transplant strawberries during Transplanting Time.

Leaf times

- Tend leafy plants (like lettuce) during these times.
- Harvest **seeds of leaf plants.**
- Transplant conifer and evergreen shrubs during Transplanting Time.
- Transplant cabbage during Transplanting Time.

Flower times

- Tend flowering plants (broccoli, roses) during these times.
- Harvest **seeds of flower plants.**
- Plant hyacinths, tulips and lilies.
- Transplant bienniels during Transplanting Time.

Root times

- Tend root plants (carrots, potatoes) during these times.
- Harvest **seeds of root plants.**
- Sow carrots, transplant onions.

Date	Planetary aspects (**Bold** = visible to naked eye)
16	♀△♆ 1^{h}
17	
18	☽☍☿ 7^{h}
19	☽☌♅ 14^{h}
20	☽☍♀ 1^{h}
21	**☽☌♃ 7^{h}**
22	☿△♄ 7^{h}
23	**☽☌♂ 21^{h}**
24	☽☍♇ 5^{h}
25	
26	
27	☽☍♄ 18^{h}
28	♂△♆ 13^{h}
29	☽☍♆ 0^{h}
30	☿☍♅ 22^{h}
31	

Planet positions in zodiac

☿ Mercury	♍	19 ♎
♀ Venus	♏	
♂ Mars	♊	28 ♋
♃ Jupiter	♉	(R)
♄ Saturn	♒	(R)
♅ Uranus	♉	(R)
♆ Neptune	♓	(R)
♇ Pluto	♑	

Planet (naked eye) visibility

Evening:
Venus

All night:
Jupiter, Saturn

Morning:
Mars

♓ Pisces ♈ Aries ♉ Taurus ♊ Gemini ♋ Cancer ♌ Leo
♍ Virgo ♎ Libra ♏ Scorpio ♐ Sagittarius ♑ Capricorn ♒ Aquarius

Control pests
(see p. 74 for details)

- **Flies:** burn fly papers at Flower times.
- **Slugs:** ash from Oct 24 2^{h} to Oct 25 17^{h}.
- Burn feathers or skins of **warm blooded pests** from Oct 19 11^{h} to Oct 21 22^{h}. *The burning (and grinding) should be completed by Oct 21 22^{h}.*

Treating cleared ground

All **cleared ground** should be treated with compost, sprayed with barrel preparation, and ploughed ready for winter.

Maria Thun's tree log preparations

- Cut **larch** logs, fill with dried **camomile** and put them into the ground between Oct 30 11^{h} and Oct 31 4^{h}.

Southern hemisphere

Southern Transplanting Time
Oct 9 to Oct 21 23^{h}

Notes

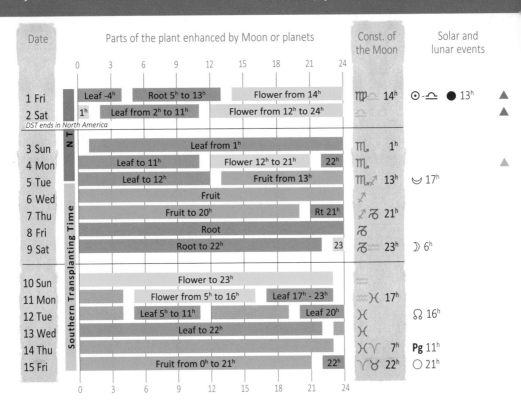

Date	Parts of the plant enhanced by Moon or planets	Const. of the Moon	Solar and lunar events
1 Fri	Leaf -4ʰ Root 5ʰ to 13ʰ Flower from 14ʰ	♍♎ 14ʰ	☉-♎ ● 13ʰ ▲
2 Sat	1ʰ Leaf from 2ʰ to 11ʰ Flower from 12ʰ to 24ʰ	♎	▲
DST ends in North America			
3 Sun	Leaf from 1ʰ	♏ 1ʰ	▲
4 Mon	Leaf to 11ʰ Flower 12ʰ to 21ʰ 22ʰ	♏	
5 Tue	Leaf to 12ʰ Fruit from 13ʰ	♏♐ 13ʰ	☋ 17ʰ
6 Wed	Fruit	♐	
7 Thu	Fruit to 20ʰ Rt 21ʰ	♐♑ 21ʰ	
8 Fri	Root	♑	
9 Sat	Root to 22ʰ 23	♑♒ 23ʰ	☽ 6ʰ
10 Sun	Flower to 23ʰ	♒	
11 Mon	Flower from 5ʰ to 16ʰ Leaf 17ʰ - 23ʰ	♒♓ 17ʰ	
12 Tue	Leaf 5ʰ to 11ʰ Leaf 20ʰ	♓	♌ 16ʰ
13 Wed	Leaf to 22ʰ	♓	
14 Thu		♓♈ 7ʰ	**Pg** 11ʰ
15 Fri	Fruit from 0ʰ to 21ʰ 22ʰ	♈♉ 22ʰ	○ 21ʰ

Southern Transplanting Time (left margin)

Transplanting Time
(time of descending Moon in northern hemisphere)
Oct 22 to Nov 5 15ʰ and Nov 18 12ʰ to Dec 2

Leaf times

- Tend leafy plants (like lettuce) during these times.
- Transplant hedges and climbing shrubs during Transplanting Time.

Root times

- Tend root plants (carrots, potatoes) during these times.
- Harvest Jerusalem artichokes, parsnips, leeks.

Fruit times

- Tend fruit plants (beans, grains, tomatoes) during these times.
- In warm regions harvest table olives.

Flower times

- Tend flowering plants (broccoli, roses) during these times.
- Cut **Advent greenery** and **Christmas trees** for transporting.
- Plant wisterias, begonias and clematis.
- Cut back rose shrubs.
- Sow sweet peas for germinating next spring.

Date	Planetary aspects (**Bold** = visible to naked eye)

1		☿△♆ 1ʰ
2		☿△♂ 8ʰ ☽⚋♄ 21ʰ
3		☽☌☿ 7ʰ ♂⚋♇ 12ʰ ♀⚋♃ 15ʰ
4		☉△♄ 18ʰ ☽⚋♃ 21ʰ
5		☽☌♀ 0ʰ
6		
7		☽☌♇ 23ʰ
8		☽⚋♂ 1ʰ
9		
10		
11		☽•♄ 2ʰ
12		☽•♆ 2ʰ
13		
14		
15		

Planet positions in zodiac

☿	Mercury	♎ 1 ♏
♀	Venus	♏ 10 ♐
♂	Mars	♋
♃	Jupiter	♉ (R)
♄	Saturn	♒ (R 15 D)
♅	Uranus	♉ (R)
♆	Neptune	♓ (R)
♇	Pluto	♑

Planet (naked eye) visibility

Evening:
Venus

All night:
Mars, Jupiter, Saturn

Morning:
–

♓	Pisces	♈	Aries	♉	Taurus	♊	Gemini	♋	Cancer	♌	Leo
♍	Virgo	♎	Libra	♏	Scorpio	♐	Sagittarius	♑	Capricorn	♒	Aquarius

NB: All zodiac symbols refer to astronomical constellations, not astrological signs (see p. 10).

Control pests
(see p. 74 for details)
- **Flies:** burn fly papers at Flower times.

Southern hemisphere
Southern Transplanting Time
Nov 5 19ʰ to Nov 18 8ʰ

Compost
If not already completed in October, all organic waste materials should be gathered and made into a **compost**. Applying the biodynamic preparations to the compost will ensure a rapid transformation and good fungal development. An application of barrel preparation will also help the composting process.

Maria Thun's tree log preparations
- Cut **oak** logs, fill with ground **oak bark** and put them into the ground on Nov 3 between 1ʰ and 18ʰ.
- Cut **birch** logs, fill with dried **yarrow** and put them into the ground on Nov 3 between 4ʰ and 21ʰ.

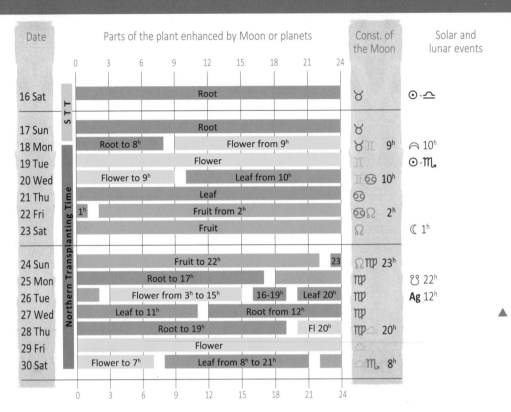

Date	Parts of the plant enhanced by Moon or planets	Const. of the Moon	Solar and lunar events
16 Sat	Root	♉	☉-♎
17 Sun	Root	♉	
18 Mon	Root to 8ʰ / Flower from 9ʰ	♉♊ 9ʰ	⌒ 10ʰ
19 Tue	Flower	♊	☉-♏
20 Wed	Flower to 9ʰ / Leaf from 10ʰ	♊♋ 10ʰ	
21 Thu	Leaf	♋	
22 Fri	1ʰ / Fruit from 2ʰ	♋♌ 2ʰ	
23 Sat	Fruit	♌	☾ 1ʰ
24 Sun	Fruit to 22ʰ / 23	♌♍ 23ʰ	
25 Mon	Root to 17ʰ	♍	☍ 22ʰ
26 Tue	Flower from 3ʰ to 15ʰ / 16–19ʰ / Leaf 20ʰ	♍	**Ag** 12ʰ
27 Wed	Leaf to 11ʰ / Root from 12ʰ	♍	
28 Thu	Root to 19ʰ / Fl 20ʰ	♍♎ 20ʰ	
29 Fri	Flower	♎	
30 Sat	Flower to 7ʰ / Leaf from 8ʰ to 21ʰ	♎♏ 8ʰ	

(Left margin: S T T — Northern Transplanting Time)

Transplanting Time
(time of descending Moon in northern hemisphere)
Nov 18 12ʰ to Dec 2

Leaf times
- Tend leafy plants (like lettuce) during these times.
- Harvest Brussels sprouts, lettuce, spinach.
- Transplant hedges and climbing shrubs during Transplanting Time.

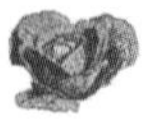

Root times
- Tend root plants (carrots, potatoes) during these times.

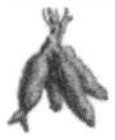

Fruit times
- Tend fruit plants (beans, grains, tomatoes) during these times.
- **Fruit and forest trees** will benefit from a spraying of horn manure and/or barrel preparation when being transplanted at Fruit times.
- Prune fruit trees and shrubs.

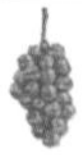

Flower times
- Tend flowering plants (broccoli, roses) during these times.
- Cut **Advent greenery** and **Christmas trees** for transporting.

Date	Planetary aspects (**Bold** = visible to naked eye)
16	$☽ ☌ ☝ 0^h$
17	$☉ ☍ ☝ 3^h$ $☽ ☍ ☿ 13^h$ $☽ ☌ ♃ 14^h$
18	$☿ ☍ ♃ 9^h$
19	$☽ ☍ ♀ 0^h$ $☉ △ ♆ 2^h$
20	$☽ ☍ ♇ 14^h$ $☽ ☌ ♂ 22^h$
21	
22	
23	
24	$☽ ☍ ♄ 0^h$
25	$☽ ☍ ♆ 6^h$
26	
27	$☉ △ ♂ 8^h$
28	
29	
30	$☽ ☍ ☝ 2^h$

Planet positions in zodiac

☿	Mercury	♏ (26 R)
♀	Venus	♐
♂	Mars	♋
♃	Jupiter	♉ (R)
♄	Saturn	♒
♅	Uranus	♉ (R)
♆	Neptune	♓ (R)
♇	Pluto	♑

Planet (naked eye) visibility

Evening:
Venus

All night:
Mars, Jupiter, Saturn

Morning:
–

♓ Pisces	♈ Aries	♉ Taurus	♊ Gemini	♋ Cancer	♌ Leo
♍ Virgo	♎ Libra	♏ Scorpio	♐ Sagittarius	♑ Capricorn	♒ Aquarius

NB: All zodiac symbols refer to astronomical constellations, not astrological signs (see p. 10).

Control pests
(see p. 74 for details)

- **Flies:** burn fly papers at Flower times.

Southern hemisphere

Southern Transplanting Time
Nov 5 to Nov 18 8^h

Compost

If not already completed in October, all organic waste materials should be gathered and made into a **compost**. Applying the biodynamic preparations to the compost will ensure a rapid transformation and good fungal development. An application of barrel preparation will also help the composting process.

Notes

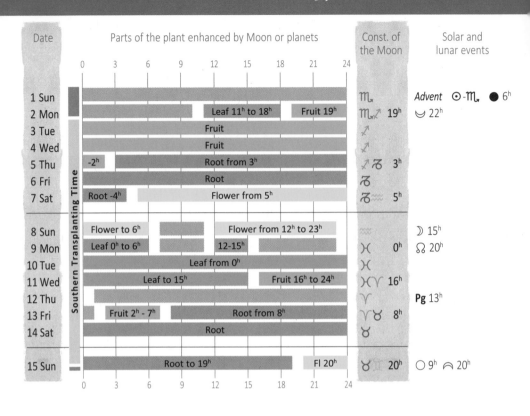

Date	Parts of the plant enhanced by Moon or planets	Const. of the Moon	Solar and lunar events
1 Sun		♏	*Advent* ☉-♏ ● 6ʰ
2 Mon	Leaf 11ʰ to 18ʰ Fruit 19ʰ	♏♐ 19ʰ	☋ 22ʰ
3 Tue	Fruit	♐	
4 Wed	Fruit	♐	
5 Thu	-2ʰ Root from 3ʰ	♐♑ 3ʰ	
6 Fri	Root	♑	
7 Sat	Root -4ʰ Flower from 5ʰ	♑♒ 5ʰ	
8 Sun	Flower to 6ʰ Flower from 12ʰ to 23ʰ	♒	☽ 15ʰ
9 Mon	Leaf 0ʰ to 6ʰ 12-15ʰ	♓ 0ʰ	☊ 20ʰ
10 Tue	Leaf from 0ʰ	♓	
11 Wed	Leaf to 15ʰ Fruit 16ʰ to 24ʰ	♓♈ 16ʰ	
12 Thu		♈	**Pg** 13ʰ
13 Fri	Fruit 2ʰ - 7ʰ Root from 8ʰ	♈♉ 8ʰ	
14 Sat	Root	♉	
15 Sun	Root to 19ʰ Fl 20ʰ	♉♊ 20ʰ	○ 9ʰ ⌢ 20ʰ

(Southern Transplanting Time — label along left axis)

Time scale: 0 3 6 9 12 15 18 21 24

Transplanting Time
(time of descending Moon in northern hemisphere)
Nov 18 to Dec 2 20ʰ
and Dec 15 22ʰ to Dec 30 3ʰ

Leaf times

- Tend leafy plants (like lettuce) during these times.
- On a mild day, prune decidous trees during Transplanting Time.

Root times

- Tend root plants (carrots, potatoes) during these times.

Fruit times

- Tend fruit plants (beans, grains, tomatoes) during these times.

Flower times

- Tend flowering plants (broccoli, roses) during these times.
- Cut **Advent greenery** and **Christmas trees** to ensure lasting fragrance.

Date

Planetary aspects
(**Bold** = visible to naked eye)

1	☽ ☌ ♃ 21ʰ ☿ ♌ 22ʰ
2	☽ ☌ ☿ 1ʰ ♀ △ ☊ 15ʰ
3	
4	☿ ☍ ♃ 10ʰ
5	☽ ☌ ♀ 0ʰ ☽ ☌ ♇ 5ʰ ☽ ☍ ♂ 15ʰ
6	☉ ☌ ☿ 2ʰ
7	♀ ☌ ♇ 14ʰ ☉ ☍ ♃ 21ʰ
8	**☽ ☌ ♄ 9ʰ**
9	**☽ ☌ ♆ 9ʰ**
10	
11	
12	♀ ☍ ♂ 11ʰ
13	☽ ☌ ☊ 8ʰ
14	☽ ☍ ☿ 4ʰ **☽ ☌ ♃ 19ʰ**
15	

Planet positions in zodiac

☿	Mercury	♏ (R 15 D)
♀	Venus	♐ 6 ♑
♂	Mars	♋ (6 R)
♃	Jupiter	♉ (R)
♄	Saturn	♒
☊	Uranus	♉ (R)
♆	Neptune	♓ (R 8 D)
♇	Pluto	♑

Planet (naked eye) visibility

Evening:
Venus, Saturn

All night:
Mars, Jupiter

Morning:
Mercury (from Dec 12)

♓	Pisces	♈	Aries	♉	Taurus	♊	Gemini	♋	Cancer
♌	Leo	♍	Virgo	♎	Libra	♏	Scorpio	♐	Sagittarius
♑	Capricorn	♒	Aquarius						

NB: All zodiac symbols refer to astronomical constellations, not astrological signs (see p. 10).

Notes

Southern hemisphere

Southern Transplanting Time
Dec 3 0ʰ to Dec 15 18ʰ and Dec 30 7ʰ to Jan 12

Harvest time for seeds *(Avoid unfavourable times)*
- **Fruit seeds:** at Fruit times.
- **Flower seeds:** at Flower times.
- **Leaf seeds:** at Leaf times.
- **Root seeds:** at Root times.

Date	Parts of the plant enhanced by Moon or planets	Const. of the Moon	Solar and lunar events

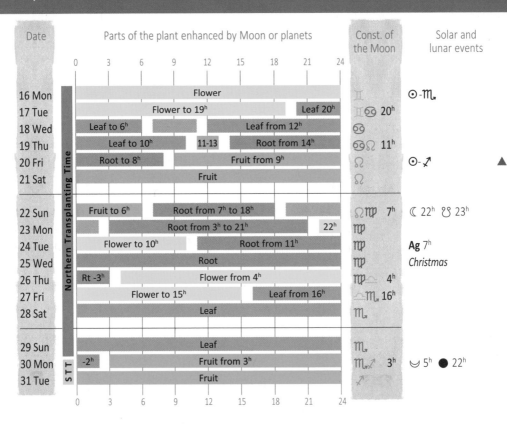

Date	Parts of the plant enhanced by Moon or planets	Const. of the Moon	Solar and lunar events
16 Mon	Flower	♊	☉-♏
17 Tue	Flower to 19h / Leaf 20h	♊ ♋ 20h	
18 Wed	Leaf to 6h / Leaf from 12h	♋	
19 Thu	Leaf to 10h / 11-13 / Root from 14h	♋ ♌ 11h	
20 Fri	Root to 8h / Fruit from 9h	♌	☉-♐ ▲
21 Sat	Fruit	♌	
22 Sun	Fruit to 6h / Root from 7h to 18h	♌♍ 7h	☾ 22h ☍ 23h
23 Mon	Root from 3h to 21h / 22h	♍	
24 Tue	Flower to 10h / Root from 11h	♍	Ag 7h
25 Wed	Root	♍	Christmas
26 Thu	Rt -3h / Flower from 4h	♍♎ 4h	
27 Fri	Flower to 15h / Leaf from 16h	♎♏ 16h	
28 Sat	Leaf	♏	
29 Sun	Leaf	♏	
30 Mon	-2h / Fruit from 3h	♏♐ 3h	☋ 5h ● 22h
31 Tue	Fruit	♐	

Northern Transplanting Time

STT

Transplanting Time
(time of descending Moon in northern hemisphere)
Dec 15 to Dec 30 3h

Fruit times
- Tend fruit plants (beans, grains, tomatoes) during these times.

Leaf times
- Tend leafy plants (like lettuce) during these times.

Flower times
- Tend flowering plants (broccoli, roses) during these times.
- Cut **Christmas trees** to ensure lasting fragrance.

Root times
- Tend root plants (carrots, potatoes) during these times.

Pruning trees and hedges
- Transplanting Time is good for **pruning trees and hedges.** Fruit trees should be pruned at Fruit or Flower times.

Date	Planetary aspects (**Bold** = visible to naked eye)
16	
17	
18	☾☍♇ 1ʰ **☾☌♂ 9ʰ**
19	☾☍♀ 0ʰ
20	**♀△♃ 2ʰ**
21	☾☍♄ 11ʰ
22	☾☍♆ 13ʰ
23	
24	
25	
26	☿☍♃ 23ʰ
27	☾☍♅ 8ʰ
28	☾☍♃ 22ʰ
29	**☾☌☿ 3ʰ**
30	
31	

Planet positions in zodiac

☿ Mercury	♏	
♀ Venus	♑	31 ♒
♂ Mars	♋	(R)
♃ Jupiter	♉	(R)
♄ Saturn	♒	
♅ Uranus	♉	30 ♈ (R)
♆ Neptune	♓	
♇ Pluto	♑	

Planet (naked eye) visibility

Evening:
Venus, Saturn

All night:
Mars, Jupiter

Morning:
Mercury

♓ Pisces ♈ Aries ♉ Taurus ♊ Gemini ♋ Cancer ♌ Leo
♍ Virgo ♎ Libra ♏ Scorpio ♐ Sagittarius ♑ Capricorn ♒ Aquarius

Notes

Southern hemisphere

Southern Transplanting Time
Dec 30 7ʰ to Jan 12

Harvest time for seeds *(Avoid unfavourable times)*
- **Fruit seeds:** at Fruit times.
- **Flower seeds:** at Flower times.
- **Leaf seeds:** at Leaf times.
- **Root seeds:** at Root times.

Control slugs: Dec 17 20ʰ to Dec 19 10ʰ.

Crop tables

The following tables suggest suitable times for sowing and harvesting particular crops. This makes it easier to find the right calendar page for detailed timings. The times are for northern hemisphere, and may need adjusting to your local climate. Between these times, the plants need tending: thinning out, transplanting, hoeing, weeding, watering, composting or manuring.

- Sow and plant in the greenhouse or under cover, depending on the season and your local climate.
- Transplant during Transplanting Time (descending Moon) at Root, Leaf, Flower or Fruit time as appropriate.
- Tend (hoeing, weeding, watering, composting) and harvest at Root, Leaf, Flower or Fruit time as appropriate.

Root vegetables

Beets

Sow	Jan	Feb	Mar	April	May	June	July	Aug	Sep	Oct	Nov	Dec
Harvest	Jan	Feb	Mar	April	May	June	July	Aug	Sep	Oct	Nov	Dec

Carrots

Sow	Jan	Feb	Mar	April	May	June	July	Aug	Sep	Oct	Nov	Dec
Harvest	Jan	Feb	Mar	April	May	June	July	Aug	Sep	Oct	Nov	Dec

Celeriac

Sow	Jan	Feb	Mar	April	May	June	July	Aug	Sep	Oct	Nov	Dec
Harvest	Jan	Feb	Mar	April	May	June	July	Aug	Sep	Oct	Nov	Dec

Garlic

Sow	Jan	Feb	Mar	April	May	June	July	Aug	Sep	Oct	Nov	Dec
Harvest	Jan	Feb	Mar	April	May	June	July	Aug	Sep	Oct	Nov	Dec

Horseradish

Sow	Jan	Feb	Mar	April	May	June	July	Aug	Sep	Oct	Nov	Dec
Harvest	Jan	Feb	Mar	April	May	June	July	Aug	Sep	Oct	Nov	Dec

Jerusalem artichoke

Sow	Jan	Feb	Mar	April	May	June	July	Aug	Sep	Oct	Nov	Dec
Harvest	Jan	Feb	Mar	April	May	June	July	Aug	Sep	Oct	Nov	Dec

Onion

Sow	Jan	Feb	Mar	April	May	June	July	Aug	Sep	Oct	Nov	Dec
Harvest	Jan	Feb	Mar	April	May	June	July	Aug	Sep	Oct	Nov	Dec

Parsnip

Sow	Jan	**Feb**	**Mar**	**April**	**May**	**June**	July	Aug	Sep	Oct	Nov	Dec
Harvest	**Jan**	**Feb**	**Mar**	**April**	May	June	July	Aug	**Sep**	**Oct**	**Nov**	**Dec**

Potato, root tubers

Sow	Jan	**Feb**	**Mar**	**April**	May	June	July	Aug	Sep	Oct	Nov	Dec
Harvest	Jan	Feb	Mar	**April**	**May**	**June**	**July**	**Aug**	**Sep**	Oct	Nov	Dec

Radish

Sow	**Jan**	**Feb**	**Mar**	**April**	**May**	**June**	**July**	**Aug**	**Sep**	**Oct**	**Nov**	**Dec**
Harvest	**Jan**	**Feb**	**Mar**	**April**	**May**	**June**	**July**	**Aug**	**Sep**	**Oct**	**Nov**	**Dec**

Salsify

Sow	Jan	Feb	**Mar**	**April**	**May**	**June**	**July**	**Aug**	Sep	Oct	Nov	Dec
Harvest	**Jan**	**Feb**	Mar	April	May	June	July	Aug	Sep	**Oct**	**Nov**	**Dec**

Shallots

Sow	Jan	Feb	Mar	April	May	June	July	Aug	**Sep**	**Oct**	Nov	Dec
Harvest	Jan	**Feb**	**Mar**	April	May	June	July	Aug	Sep	Oct	Nov	Dec

Leaf plants

Asparagus

Sow	**Jan**	**Feb**	**Mar**	**April**	**May**	June	July	Aug	Sep	Oct	Nov	Dec
Harvest	Jan	Feb	**Mar**	**April**	**May**	**June**	**July**	**Aug**	**Sep**	Oct	Nov	Dec

Bok choy *see* Chinese cabbage

Brussels sprouts

Sow	Jan	Feb	**Mar**	**April**	**May**	June	July	Aug	Sep	Oct	Nov	Dec
Harvest	**Jan**	**Feb**	**Mar**	April	May	June	July	Aug	**Sep**	**Oct**	**Nov**	**Dec**

Cabbage

Sow	**Jan**	**Feb**	**Mar**	**April**	**May**	**June**	**July**	**Aug**	**Sep**	**Oct**	Nov	Dec
Harvest	Jan	Feb	Mar	April	**May**	**June**	**July**	**Aug**	**Sep**	**Oct**	**Nov**	**Dec**

Celery

Sow	Jan	Feb	**Mar**	**April**	**May**	June	July	Aug	Sep	Oct	Nov	Dec
Harvest	Jan	Feb	Mar	April	May	June	July	**Aug**	**Sep**	**Oct**	**Nov**	**Dec**

Chard

Sow	Jan	Feb	Mar	**April**	**May**	**June**	July	Aug	Sep	Oct	Nov	Dec
Harvest	Jan	Feb	Mar	April	May	June	**July**	**Aug**	**Sep**	**Oct**	**Nov**	Dec

Chicory (endives)

Sow	Jan	Feb	Mar	April	**May**	**June**	July	Aug	Sep	Oct	Nov	Dec
Harvest	Jan	Feb	Mar	April	May	**June**	**July**	**Aug**	**Sep**	**Oct**	**Nov**	**Dec**

Chinese cabbage (pe-tsai, bok choy)

Sow	Jan	Feb	Mar	April	**May**	**June**	**July**	**Aug**	**Sep**	Oct	Nov	Dec
Harvest	Jan	Feb	Mar	April	May	June	July	Aug	**Sep**	**Oct**	**Nov**	**Dec**

Corn salad *see* Lamb's lettuce
Curly kale (green cabbage)

Sow	Jan	Feb	Mar	April	May	June	July	Aug	Sep	Oct	Nov	Dec
Harvest	Jan	Feb	Mar	April	May	June	July	Aug	Sep	Oct	Nov	Dec

Endives *see* Chicory
Grass (lawns)

Sow	Jan	Feb	Mar	April	May	June	July	Aug	Sep	Oct	Nov	Dec
Mow	Jan	Feb	Mar	April	May	June	July	Aug	Sep	Oct	Nov	Dec

Green cabbage *see* Curly kale
Kohlrabi

Sow	Jan	Feb	Mar	April	May	June	July	Aug	Sep	Oct	Nov	Dec
Harvest	Jan	Feb	Mar	April	May	June	July	Aug	Sep	Oct	Nov	Dec

Lamb's lettuce (corn salad)

Sow	Jan	Feb	Mar	April	May	June	July	Aug	Sep	Oct	Nov	Dec
Harvest	Jan	Feb	Mar	April	May	June	July	Aug	Sep	Oct	Nov	Dec

Leaf herbs

Sow	Jan	Feb	Mar	April	May	June	July	Aug	Sep	Oct	Nov	Dec
Harvest	Jan	Feb	Mar	April	May	June	July	Aug	Sep	Oct	Nov	Dec

Leek

Sow	Jan	Feb	Mar	April	May	June	July	Aug	Sep	Oct	Nov	Dec
Harvest	Jan	Feb	Mar	April	May	June	July	Aug	Sep	Oct	Nov	Dec

Lettuce, crisphead (iceberg) lettuce

Sow	Jan	Feb	Mar	April	May	June	July	Aug	Sep	Oct	Nov	Dec
Harvest	Jan	Feb	Mar	April	May	June	July	Aug	Sep	Oct	Nov	Dec

Lettuce, winter

Sow	Jan	Feb	Mar	April	May	June	July	Aug	Sep	Oct	Nov	Dec
Harvest	Jan	Feb	Mar	April	May	June	July	Aug	Sep	Oct	Nov	Dec

Red cabbage

Sow	Jan	Feb	Mar	April	May	June	July	Aug	Sep	Oct	Nov	Dec
Harvest	Jan	Feb	Mar	April	May	June	July	Aug	Sep	Oct	Nov	Dec

Rhubarb

Sow	Jan	Feb	Mar	April	May	June	July	Aug	Sep	Oct	Nov	Dec
Harvest	Jan	Feb	Mar	April	May	June	July	Aug	Sep	Oct	Nov	Dec

Spinach

Sow	Jan	Feb	Mar	April	May	June	July	Aug	Sep	Oct	Nov	Dec
Harvest	Jan	Feb	Mar	April	May	June	July	Aug	Sep	Oct	Nov	Dec

Flower plants

Artichoke (globe)

Sow	Jan	Feb	Mar	April	May	June	July	Aug	Sep	Oct	Nov	Dec
Harvest	Jan	Feb	Mar	April	May	June	July	Aug	Sep	Oct	Nov	Dec

Broccoli

Sow	Jan	Feb	Mar	April	May	June	July	Aug	Sep	Oct	Nov	Dec
Harvest	Jan	Feb	Mar	April	May	June	July	Aug	Sep	Oct	Nov	Dec

Cauliflower

Sow	Jan	Feb	Mar	April	May	June	July	Aug	Sep	Oct	Nov	Dec
Harvest	Jan	Feb	Mar	April	May	June	July	Aug	Sep	Oct	Nov	Dec

Flower bulbs

Sow	Jan	Feb	Mar	April	May	June	July	Aug	Sep	Oct	Nov	Dec
Harvest	Jan	Feb	Mar	April	May	June	July	Aug	Sep	Oct	Nov	Dec

Flowers, flowery herbs

Sow	Jan	Feb	Mar	April	May	June	July	Aug	Sep	Oct	Nov	Dec
Harvest	Jan	Feb	Mar	April	May	June	July	Aug	Sep	Oct	Nov	Dec

Rose

Sow	Jan	Feb	Mar	April	May	June	July	Aug	Sep	Oct	Nov	Dec
Harvest	Jan	Feb	Mar	April	May	June	July	Aug	Sep	Oct	Nov	Dec

Sunflower

Sow	Jan	Feb	Mar	April	May	June	July	Aug	Sep	Oct	Nov	Dec
Harvest	Jan	Feb	Mar	April	May	June	July	Aug	Sep	Oct	Nov	Dec

Fruit plants

Aubergine (eggplant)

Sow	Jan	Feb	Mar	April	May	June	July	Aug	Sep	Oct	Nov	Dec
Harvest	Jan	Feb	Mar	April	May	June	July	Aug	Sep	Oct	Nov	Dec

Barley *see* Grain

Beans, lentils

Sow	Jan	Feb	Mar	April	May	June	July	Aug	Sep	Oct	Nov	Dec
Harvest	Jan	Feb	Mar	April	May	June	July	Aug	Sep	Oct	Nov	Dec

Corn *see* Maize

Courgette (zucchini)

Sow	Jan	Feb	Mar	April	May	June	July	Aug	Sep	Oct	Nov	Dec
Harvest	Jan	Feb	Mar	April	May	June	July	Aug	Sep	Oct	Nov	Dec

Cucumber

Sow	Jan	Feb	Mar	April	May	June	July	Aug	Sep	Oct	Nov	Dec
Harvest	Jan	Feb	Mar	April	May	June	July	Aug	Sep	Oct	Nov	Dec

Eggplant *see* Aubergine

Grains (wheat, barley, rye, oats, etc.)

	Jan	Feb	Mar	April	May	June	July	Aug	Sep	Oct	Nov	Dec
Sow	Jan	Feb	Mar	April	May	**June**	**July**	**Aug**	**Sep**	Oct	Nov	Dec
Harvest	**Jan**	**Feb**	**Mar**	**April**	**May**	June	July	Aug	**Sep**	**Oct**	**Nov**	**Dec**

Maize (corn, sweetcorn)

	Jan	Feb	Mar	April	May	June	July	Aug	Sep	Oct	Nov	Dec
Sow	Jan	Feb	**Mar**	**April**	**May**	**June**	July	Aug	Sep	Oct	Nov	Dec
Harvest	Jan	Feb	Mar	April	May	June	**July**	**Aug**	**Sep**	**Oct**	**Nov**	**Dec**

Melon

	Jan	Feb	Mar	April	May	June	July	Aug	Sep	Oct	Nov	Dec
Sow	Jan	**Feb**	**Mar**	**April**	May	June	July	Aug	Sep	Oct	Nov	Dec
Harvest	Jan	Feb	Mar	April	May	June	**July**	**Aug**	**Sep**	Oct	Nov	Dec

Oats *see* Grain

Paprika, chilli and sweet pepper

	Jan	Feb	Mar	April	May	June	July	Aug	Sep	Oct	Nov	Dec
Sow	**Jan**	**Feb**	**Mar**	April	May	June	July	Aug	Sep	Oct	Nov	Dec
Harvest	Jan	Feb	Mar	April	May	June	**July**	**Aug**	**Sep**	**Oct**	Nov	Dec

Pea

	Jan	Feb	Mar	April	May	June	July	Aug	Sep	Oct	Nov	Dec
Sow	**Jan**	**Feb**	**Mar**	**April**	**May**	June	July	Aug	Sep	**Oct**	**Nov**	**Dec**
Harvest	Jan	Feb	**Mar**	**April**	**May**	**June**	**July**	Aug	Sep	Oct	Nov	Dec

Pumpkin *see* Squash

Runner bean (pole bean)

	Jan	Feb	Mar	April	May	June	July	Aug	Sep	Oct	Nov	Dec
Sow	Jan	Feb	Mar	April	**May**	**June**	**July**	Aug	Sep	Oct	Nov	Dec
Harvest	Jan	Feb	Mar	April	May	June	**July**	**Aug**	**Sep**	**Oct**	Nov	Dec

Rye *see* Grain

Soya

	Jan	Feb	Mar	April	May	June	July	Aug	Sep	Oct	Nov	Dec
Sow	Jan	Feb	Mar	**April**	**May**	**June**	July	Aug	Sep	Oct	Nov	Dec
Harvest	Jan	Feb	Mar	April	**May**	**June**	**July**	**Aug**	**Sep**	**Oct**	**Nov**	**Dec**

Squash (pumpkin)

	Jan	Feb	Mar	April	May	June	July	Aug	Sep	Oct	Nov	Dec
Sow	Jan	Feb	**Mar**	**April**	**May**	**June**	July	Aug	Sep	Oct	Nov	Dec
Harvest	Jan	Feb	Mar	April	May	**June**	**July**	**Aug**	**Sep**	**Oct**	Nov	Dec

Strawberry

	Jan	Feb	Mar	April	May	June	July	Aug	Sep	Oct	Nov	Dec
Sow	Jan	Feb	Mar	April	May	June	July	**Aug**	**Sep**	**Oct**	Nov	Dec
Harvest	Jan	Feb	Mar	**April**	**May**	**June**	**July**	**Aug**	**Sep**	Oct	Nov	Dec

Sweetcorn *see* Maize

Tomato

	Jan	Feb	Mar	April	May	June	July	Aug	Sep	Oct	Nov	Dec
Sow	Jan	**Feb**	**Mar**	**April**	May	June	July	Aug	Sep	Oct	Nov	Dec
Harvest	Jan	Feb	Mar	April	May	**June**	**July**	**Aug**	**Sep**	**Oct**	Nov	Dec

Wheat *see* Grain

Zucchini *see* Courgette

Companion planting

Plants grown in close proximity influence each other, and the technique of companion planting is sometimes used for pest control, pollination or simply maximising space. For instance, leeks keep away carrot flies and carrots discourage leek moths.

Maria Thun was sceptical about companion planting, as the plants grown together are often different types (leeks are Leaf plants and carrots are Root plants). When trying to enhance their growth through the activity of hoeing and general care of the plants at Leaf or Root times, it is impossible to do justice to both plants. One or the other crop will suffer. Therefore work should be done on prime crops at times that are most beneficial to them.

The following table (based on Philbrick & Gregg, *Companion Plants*) shows which plants help vegetable, fruit, cereal and herb crops to thrive by encouraging growth, deterring pests or preventing disease.

Prime crop *Companion crops*	*Prime crop* *Companion crops*
Apple tree chive, nasturtium, vetch, wallflower	**Broccoli** (*see also* Cabbage) beetroot (beet), nasturtium
Asparagus parsley, tomato	**Cabbage, Brussels sprout, kale** beetroot (beet), camomile,
Aubergine (eggplant) green (bush) bean	celery, dill, hyssop, lettuce, mint, potato, rosemary, sage, thyme
Bean (all types) beetroot (beet), cabbage, carrot, cauliflower, corn (maize), cucumber, marigold, potato	**Carrot** chive, leek, lettuce, onion, radish, rosemary, sage
Bean, broad (fava) corn (maize), oat, potato	**Cauliflower** (*see also* Cabbage) celery
Bean, green (bush) cabbage, celery, corn (maize), cucumber, potato, strawberry, summer savory	**Celeriac** leek
Bean, runner (pole) corn (maize), radish	**Celery** green (bush) bean, leek, onion tomato
Beets, beetroot cabbage, green (bush) bean, lettuce, kohlrabi, onion	**Chervil** radish, yarrow
	Citrus tree guava, live (evergreen) oak, rubber tree

Prime crop Companion crops	Prime crop Companion crops
Corn (maize) bean, cucumber, pea, potato, wheat	**Potato** bean (except butter bean/ lima), cabbage, corn, dead nettle (henbit), flax, horseradish, mari-gold, nasturtium, pea, sainfoin (esparcet)
Cucumber cabbage, celeriac, corn, green (bush) bean, kohlrabi, lettuce, potato, radish, sunflower	**Radish** chervil, lettuce, kohlrabi, nastur-tium, pea, runner (pole) bean
Fruit tree chive, garlic, horseradish, legumes, mustard, nasturtium, stinging nettle, tansy, vetch	**Rosemary** sage, yarrow
Garlic rose	**Rye** pansy, vetch
Grapevine elm tree, hyssop, legumes, mulberry, mustard	**Sage** rosemary, yarrow
Herbs stinging nettle, yarrow	**Spinach** strawberry
Kale *see* Cabbage	**Squash (pumpkin)** corn (maize), nasturtium
Kohlrabi (*see also* Cabbage) beetroot (beet), lettuce, onion	**Strawberry** borage, green (bush) bean, let-tuce, spinach
Leek carrot, celeriac, celery	**Tomato** asparagus, celery, marigold, parsley, stinging nettle
Lettuce beetroot (beet), cabbage, camo-mile, carrot, strawberry	**Turnip, swede (rutabaga)** pea
Melon corn (maize)	**Wheat** corn (maize), sainfoin (esparcet)
Oat vetch	
Onion beetroot (beet), carrot, celery, lettuce, summer savory	**Border plants that benefit most vegetables:** bean, borage, camomile, chervil, chive, dead nettle (henbit), dill, lavender, hyssop, lovage, mar-joram, parsley, pea, sage, sainfoin (esparcet), tarragon, thyme, vale-rian, hyssop, lemon balm, yarrow (not fennel or wormwood)
Pea bean, carrot, cucumber, radish, potato, corn (maize), turnip/ swede (rutabaga)	
Peach tree tansy	

Biodynamic preparations

The compost preparations

The classic preparation plants used by biodynamic practitioners for compost preparations are picked, dried and inserted into animal sheaths (skull, bladder, etc.). For more see Further Reading, p. 96.

- Pick *dandelions* in the morning at Flower times as soon as they are open, while the centre of the flowers are still tightly packed.
- Pick *yarrow* at Fruit times when the Sun is in Leo (around the middle of August).
- Pick *camomile* at Flower times just before midsummer. If they are harvested too late, seeds will begin to form and there are often grubs in the hollow heads.
- Collect *stinging nettles* when the first flowers are opening, usually around midsummer. Harvest the whole plants without roots at Flower times.
- Pick *valerian* at Flower times around midsummer.
- Collect *oak bark* at Root times. The pithy material below the bark should not be used.

All the flowers (except valerian) should be laid out on paper and dried in the shade.

Maria Thun's tree bark preparations

Many of the classic biodynamic preparations require the use of animal organs. With the onset of BSE, using them became more difficult. This led Maria Thun to develop preparations using the bark of trees instead (see p. 93). They are not counted among the biodynamic preparations developed by Rudolf Steiner, but they do build on indications gained through his approach and can be used in biodynamic agriculture.

The plants should be picked and dried as indicated above. The logs for the bark need to be cut, filled and buried in the ground in accordance with lunar and planetary rhythms. These times (indicated in the calendar) need to be kept with some precision otherwise the preparations may be less effective. Since these planetary constellations do not occur regularly and in some years do not arise at all, it is worth making sufficient preparations to last more than one year. They should be stored, like all biodynamic preparations, in pots surrounded by peat.

The spray preparations

There are two spray preparations – horn manure and horn silica. Maria Thun's research showed the best times to apply these.

Horn manure is most effective when sprayed on the soil, not on the plants, and is applied three times: before sowing, during sowing and after sowing. Its effect is to help the seeds and young seedlings to orientate themselves better in the soil.

Horn silica is best sprayed at Fruit times on crops beginning to shoot and form ears. Its effect is to enhance the vitality of the plant. Like horn manure, it must be stirred for a whole hour but is then only effective for up to four hours. This means that it must be sprayed out as soon as possible after stirring. The best time for spraying is immediately after sunrise, so that entails an early start.

Animal and insect pests, fungal problems

When dealing with the often significant issue of animal or insect pests, there is generally no need to reach for biological and chemical pesticides. The first step is to familiarise yourself with the conditions and habits of the pest, and to rectify any management errors that have been made. If despite this, the pest continues, it can be contained within its natural limits by using the ashes of its own burnt remains.

Snails and slugs

For an average infestation, collect between fifty and sixty animals. When the Moon is in Cancer put them in a bucket of water filled to the brim with a close fitting lid. Let it stand for four weeks until the Moon is again in Cancer, then spray the liquid where slugs and snails are a problem. Where slugs and snails are a huge problem, add some

One species, the Great Grey or Leopard Slug (Limex maximus) should be encouraged, as it feeds primarily on decaying plant remains and on the eggs of other slugs. This rare slug is 10–18 cm (4–7 in) long and unlike other large brown slugs, it is only active at night.

twenty slugs to the horn silica preparation and stir it for an hour before spraying over the affected ground where slugs and snails are wont to feed. The light effect of silica is very disagreeable to slugs. Spray three times successively.

Mice, other mammals, birds and insects

Take a few skins of mammals, a few bird feathers, or for insects take fifty or sixty insects. Burn them in a wood fire (don't use grilling charcoal) during the appropriate planetary aspect, indicated in the 'Control pests' notes on the calendar pages. Ensure the fire is glowing hot. Lay dry feathers, skins or dead pests on the embers. After they have cooled, collect the light grey ash and grind for an hour with a pestle and mortar, as this increases its efficacy. The burning and grinding should be completed within the time indicated under Pest Control.

The ashes can be kept in an airtight jar until you need them. Label the jar with type of ash, potency and date.

The ground-up ash can then be potentised (diluted) later.

To make a liquid for spraying, place one gram (or level teaspoon) of this ground-up ash in a small bottle with 9 ml (grams, or teaspoons) of water and shake vigorously for three minutes. This is the first decimal potency (D1 or X1). Add a further 90 ml of water and shake again for three minutes. This is the second decimal potency, D2 or X2. Repeating this procedure until D8 (X8) would produce 100,000 litres (26,000 gallons). It is therefore advisable to proceed until D4 and then start again using smaller quantities (always diluting in the ratio of 1 to 9).

Alternatively the ground-up ash can be diluted with pure wood ash to make a dry ash 'pepper' for spreading on the affected area. Instead of diluting and shaking with water, use wood ash in the same proportions as water above, to make a D8 potency.

Burning skins in a wood oven

Burning in the field

Grinding the ash

Apply the liquid version as a fine mist for three evenings in succession, either using a backpack sprayer, or for large areas using a tractor-mounted sprayer. For the dry version a simple peppershaker can be used for very small areas. For larger areas, use a sowing machine with a piece of rolled-up paper set in the machine to ensure that only a minute amount of ash is released at a time.

Maria Thun advised the D8 potency was as effective as the undiluted ground-up ash, but had the advantage that a far larger area could be treated. In comparative farm trials, in both cases the animal pests remained away from the cultivated fields. The effect of deer ash could be clearly observed on an unfenced clover field where the deer had grazed the clover in the surrounding fields but not within 2 metres (7 ft) of the trial area.

Where pests occur in large numbers good results are obtained by burning them on the site where they have been found. Flea beetle and apple blossom weevil can be caught with fly papers for example and burnt on site.

Fungal problems

The function of fungus in nature is to break down dying organic materials. It appears amongst our crops when unripe manure compost or uncomposted animal by-products such as horn and bone meal are used, but also when seeds are harvested during unfavourable constellations: according to Steiner, 'When Moon forces are working too strongly on the Earth.'

Tea can be made from horsetail (*Equisetum arvense*) and sprayed on to the soil where affected plants are growing. This draws the fungal level back down into the ground where it belongs.

The plants can be strengthened by spraying stinging nettle tea on the leaves. This will promote good assimilation, stimulate the flow of sap and help fungal diseases to disappear.

Sowing and felling times for trees and shrubs

Sowing times

We can calculate optimal times for sowing seeds by looking at the Moon's position in the zodiac, depending on the part of the tree or shrub to be enhanced. You can use this method for any trees and shrubs not mentioned here. Sowing times shown here depend on planetary aspects that encourage vitality of the species; they are not specific to either northern or southern hemispheres or to any climatic region.

Sowing times are different from Transplanting Times. Seedlings should be transplanted during the descending Moon (also called Transplanting Time) when the Moon is in a constellation corresponding to the part of the tree to to be enhanced. It is important to remember that seedlings need to be sufficiently mature to withstand the winter. The time of sowing should therefore be adapted to local conditions and take account of the germination habit of each tree species.

Note: some species (marked in **bold**) appear in two groups.

*Alder, **Apricot**, Elm, **Larch**, **Peach**:*
  July 2 20^h to July 3 13^h
  Oct 30 11^h to Oct 31 4^h
  Nov 17 22^h to Nov 18 15^h
  Dec 3 23^h to Dec 4 16^h
  Dec 26 12^h to Dec 27 5^h.

*Apple, **Apricot**, Copper beech, Damson, Maple, Olive, **Peach**, **Sweet chestnut**, Walnut:*
  Nov 3 4^h to 21^h
  Nov 17 22^h to Nov 18 15^h
  Dec 3 23^h to Dec 4 16^h
  Dec 7 10^h to Dec 8 3^h
  Dec 26 12^h to Dec 27 5^h.

*Ash, **Cedar**, **Fir**, Hazel, **Mirabelle plum**, Rowan, **Spruce**:*
  July 22 18^h to July 23 11^h
  Sep 7 17^h to Sep 8 10^h *(also Hawthorn)*
  Sep 20 13^h to Sep 21 6^h
  Nov 16 16^h to Nov 17 9^h *(also Hawthorn)*
  Dec 7 10^h to Dec 8 3^h.

*Beech, **Cedar**, **Fir**, Hornbeam, Juniper, Palm, Pine, Plum, Quince, Sloe, **Spruce**, Thuja:*
  Aug 18 22^h to Aug 19 15^h
  Sep 7 17^h to Sep 8 10^h.

*Birch, **Larch**, Lime tree, **Mirabelle plum**, Pear, Robinia, Willow:*
  July 12 3^h to 17^h
  Aug 18 22^h to Aug 19 15^h
  Aug 28 10^h to Aug 29 3^h *(also Magnolia)*
  Oct 14 11^h to 15^h & 21^h to Oct 15 4^h
  Nov 3 4^h to 21^h.

Blackcurrant:
  Oct 14 11^h to 15^h & 21^h to Oct 15 4^h
  Oct 30 11^h to Oct 31 4^h
  Nov 16 16^h to Nov 17 9^h
  Dec 20 20^h to Dec 21 9^h.

*Cherry, Chestnut, Horse chestnut (Buckeye), Oak, **Sweet chestnut**, Yew:*
  Nov 3 1^h to 18^h *(also Common laurel).*

Lilac, Poplar, Sallow, Snowberry:
  Oct 14 11^h to 15^h & 21^h to Oct 15 4^h
  Oct 30 11^h to Oct 31 4^h.

Felling times

The quality and durability of cut timber can be affected by the felling time. The dates below show optimum times for different groups of trees.

If a large number of these trees need to be felled in a short time, use the time indicated to cut the bark all around the trunk to stop sap flow. The actual felling can be done later.

Trees which are not listed should be felled at the end of the growing season at Flower times.

Note that some species (marked in **bold**) appear in two groups.

Alder, **Apricot**, Elm, **Larch, Peach:**
Jan 18 22^h to Jan 19 13^h
Jan 28 10^h to 24^h (also Blackcurrant)
June 4 0^h to 9^h
June 26 12^h to 21^h
July 2 6^h to 15^h (also Magnolia)
Oct 8 0^h to 18^h
Oct 22 1^h to 10^h
Oct 31 19^h to Nov 1 4^h (also Magnolia)
Nov 2 2^h to 11^h.

Apple, **Apricot**, Copper beech, Damson, Maple, Olive, **Peach, Sweet chestnut,** Walnut:
Jan 11 23^h to Jan 12 14^h
Jan 18 22^h to Jan 19 13^h
Jan 28 13^h to Jan 29 4^h
June 2 20^h to June 3 6^h
Sep 14 18^h to Sep 15 12^h
Oct 8 0^h to 18^h
Oct 13 19^h to Oct 14 10^h
Dec 19 14^h to Dec 20 8^h.

Ash, **Cedar, Fir,** Hazel, **Mirabelle plum,** Rowan, **Spruce:**
Jan 9 18^h to Jan 10 3^h (also Blackcurrant)
May 22 9^h to 18^h
July 10 21^h to July 11 6^h

July 21 21^h to July 22 6^h
Sep 19 8^h to 17^h (also Blackcurrant)
Sep 22 0^h to 9^h
Oct 13 19^h to Oct 14 10^h
Nov 4 12^h to 21^h
Nov 18 20^h to Nov 19 5^h
Nov 26 20^h to Nov 27 11^h.

Beech, **Cedar, Fir,** Hornbeam, Juniper, Palm, Pine, Plum, Quince, Sloe, **Spruce,** Thuja:
June 26 12^h to 21^h;
July 2 19^h to July 3 5^h
July 10 21^h to July 11 6^h
Sep 29 16^h to Sep 30 7^h
Oct 4 10^h to 20^h
Oct 22 1^h to 10^h
Nov 4 12^h to 21^h.

Birch, **Larch,** Lime tree, **Mirabelle plum,** Pear, Robinia, Willow:
Jan 28 13^h to Jan 29 4^h
Feb 7 14^h to 24^h (also Blackcurrant)
May 25 4^h to 14^h
July 2 19^h to July 3 5^h
July 11 8^h to 18^h (also Magnolia)
Aug 27 0^h to 10^h (also Blackcurrant)
Aug 29 8^h to 18^h
Sep 14 18^h to Sep 15 12^h
Oct 4 10^h to 20^h
Oct 8 3^h to 13^h
Dec 2 11^h to 18^h (also Blackcurrant)
Dec 19 14^h to Dec 20 8^h.

Cherry, Chestnut, Horse chestnut (Buckeye), Oak, **Sweet chestnut,** Yew:
Jan 11 23^h to Jan 12 14^h
Jan 29 12^h to Jan 30 3^h
July 21 16^h to July 22 7^h
Sep 29 16^h to Sep 30 7^h
Oct 8 3^h to 13^h
Oct 28 1^h to 16^h
Nov 2 2^h to 11^h
Nov 26 20^h to Nov 27 11^h.

Lilac, Poplar, Sallow, Snowberry:
Jan 28 10^h to 24^h
Feb 7 14^h to 24^h
Aug 27 0^h to 10^h
Dec 2 11^h to 18^h.

Beekeeping

Matthias Thun

Bees are also influenced by the movement of the Moon. By open-ing and closing the beehive or skep in rhythm with the Moon, the beekeeper can directly affect the bees' activity. A beekeeping panel is shown on relevant calendar pages.

Constellation	Sign	Element (Type)	Bees' activity	Weather tendency
Pisces	♓	Water (Leaf)	Making honey	Damp
Aries	♈	Warmth (Fruit)	Gathering nectar	Warm/hot
Taurus	♉	Earth (Root)	Building comb	Cool/cold
Gemini	♊	Light (Flower)	Gathering pollen	Airy/bright
Cancer	♋	Water (Leaf)	Making honey	Damp
Leo	♌	Warmth (Fruit)	Gathering nectar	Warm/hot
Virgo	♍	Earth (Root)	Building comb	Cool/cold
Libra	♎	Light (Flower)	Gathering pollen	Airy/bright
Scorpio	♏	Water (Leaf)	Making honey	Damp
Sagittarius	♐	Warmth (Fruit)	Gathering nectar	Warm/hot
Capricorn	♑	Earth (Root)	Building comb	Cool/cold
Aquarius	♒	Light (Flower)	Gathering pollen	Airy/bright

The care of bees

A colony of bees lives in its hive closed off from the outside world. For extra protection against harmful influences, the inside of the hive is sealed with propolis. The link with the wider surroundings is made by the bees that fly in and out of the hive.

To make good use of cosmic rhythms, the beekeeper needs to create the right conditions in much the same way as the gardener or farmer does with the plants. The gardener works the soil and in so doing allows cosmic forces to penetrate it via the air. These forces can then be taken up and used by the plants until the soil is next moved.

When the beekeeper opens up the hive, the sealing layer of propolis is broken. This creates a disturbance, as a result of which lunar and plan-etary forces can influence the life of the hive until the next intervention by the beekeeper. By this means the beekeeper can directly mediate cosmic forces to the bees.

It is not insignificant which forces of the universe are brought into play when the hive is opened. The beekeeper can consciously intervene by choosing days for working with the hive that will help the colony to develop and build up its food reserves. The bees will then reward the beekeeper by providing a portion of their harvest in the form of honey.

- *Earth-Root* times can be selected for opening the hive if the bees need to do more building.
- *Light-Flower* times encourage brood activity and colony development.
- *Warmth-Fruit* times stimulate the collection of nectar.
- *Water-Leaf* times are unsuitable for working in the hive or for the removal and processing of honey.

Varroa

Since the late 1970s the varroa mite has affected virtually every bee colony in Europe. Following a number of comparative trials Maria Thun recommend burning and making an ash of the varroa mite (as described on pp. 74f). After dynamising it for one hour, the ash should be put in a salt cellar and sprinkled lightly between the combs. The ash should be made and sprinkled when the Sun and Moon are in Taurus (May/June).

To strengthen the brood, small amounts of ash can also be sprinkled on the brood whenever an inspection is carried out .

Applying the varroa ash using a salt cellar

Feeding bees in preparation for winter

Herbal teas are recommended as supplements in the feeding of bees prior to winter. They are all plants that have proved their value over many years.

Three grams (1 tablespoon) of each dried herb and half a litre (½ quart) of the prepared teas is enough to produce 100 litres (25 gal) of liquid feed. This is a particularly important treatment in years when there are large amounts of honeydew.

Yarrow, camomile, dandelion and valerian are made by pouring boiling water over the flowers, allowing them to brew for fifteen minutes and then straining them. Stinging nettle, horsetail and oak bark are placed in cold water, brought slowly to the boil and simmered for fifteen minutes.

Two swarms have settled on a tree

Moon diagrams

The diagrams overleaf show for each month the daily position (evenings GMT) of the Moon against the stars and other planets. For viewing in the southern hemisphere, turn the diagrams upside down.

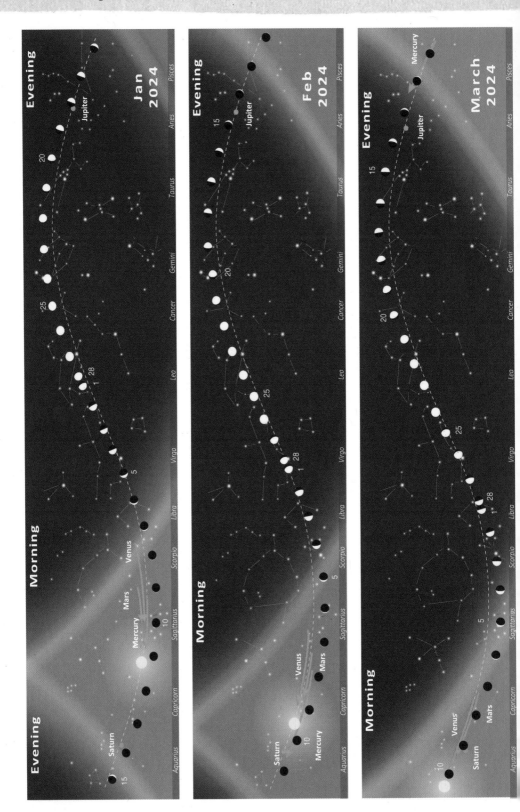

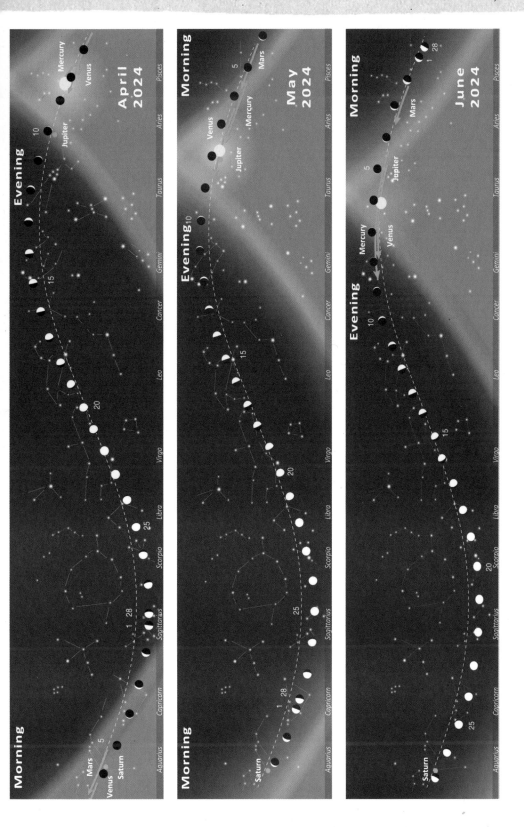

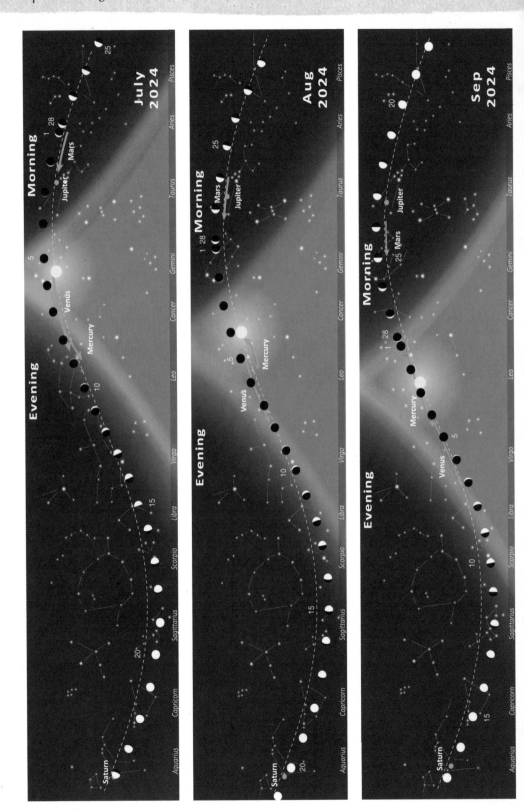

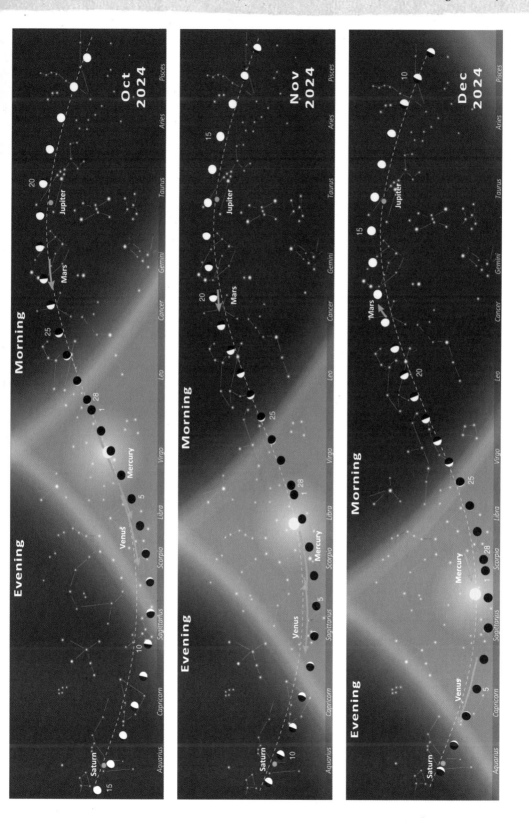

Maria Thun

April 24, 1922 –February 9, 2012

Titia Thun

Maria Thun was an ambitious woman whose lifelong quest for knowledge continuously raised new questions, and the work she undertook had a profound influence on her and the people she was associated with.

She grew up in a small farming household in Hessen, Germany, with everyone doing their bit to ensure the farm could function and feed them all. In those days it was rare for girls of her background to go beyond primary school. This did not, however, diminish her desire to learn, and she took every possible opportunity to do so. Her grandfather was the village sower and her father taught her about plants and to appreciate the influence of heavenly bodies and the weather on plant growth.

In the early 1940s she met Walter Thun, an artist who later became her husband. They had two children, Christina and Matthias. Through Walter Thun she learned about anthroposophy and this opened up a whole new world that could at last satisfy her thirst for knowledge. She also found a new connection to agriculture during this time and developed a great love for the ideas of biodynamic agriculture. She began to take part in events arranged by the Biodynamic Society in Germany (Forschungsring) and to study Rudolf Steiner's Agriculture Course with Franz Rulni who had attended these lectures himself.

Franz Rulni had produced a sowing and planting calendar that included Rudolf Steiner's suggestions along with country lore. Using this calendar Maria began her research with radishes. She sowed the radishes in a long seed bed over an extended period, which the calendar indicated as being favourable. When the first leaves had formed she found great variability between the different plants sown in the early days. The later sowings, however, did not show this variability and were far more uniform. Rulni, though fascinated by this observation, could not explain the phenomenon.

After further study of the Agriculture Course, Maria realised that if the cosmos is to influence the plant via the soil as described, then the soil should be cultivated before sowing. This insight led her to carry out daily sowings in the following year. She cultivated the soil before each sowing and found that the leaf form and growth habit of the radishes changed every two or three days.

By checking the astronomical calendar produced by the Goetheanum in Dornach, Switzerland, she discovered that the growth of her radishes changed whenever the Moon passed from one constellation into the next. The results she came to were as follows.

- When the Moon was in Virgo, Capricorn or Taurus, the radishes had a strong and fulsome root;
- when in Gemini, Libra and Aquarius, the flowering process was well developed;
- when in Cancer, Scorpio or Pisces it was the leaves that were particularly well developed;
- when the Moon was in Leo, Sagittarius and Aries there appeared to be a positive influence on fruit and seed formation.

This division into root, flower, leaf and fruit or seed formation was confirmed repeatedly in subsequent years using other plant species.

In time it became clear that other astronomical factors were also at work, and more extensive trials would be needed to understand them. She needed a larger area than her own small garden. Eventually she was able to lease some land near Marburg, Hessen.

At that time this kind of research was mostly water-based germination trials: seeds were germinated in Petri dishes to observe differences in germination. Since Maria was interested in how the plants developed beyond germination and how cosmic influences affected them over a longer time period, germination trials alone would not achieve much. Furthermore, an important process in her trials was the collecting and sowing of the seeds of her trial plants to assess their germination and quality in the following year.

In the course of such follow-on trials some unexpected discoveries were made, for instance about the effects of planetary occultations, that is, when the Moon passes in front of a planet, hiding it.

Maria Thun was now gaining more recognition. She had increasing numbers of visitors who were impressed by her work, although some expressed doubts: were the results not mainly due to soil quality? The

Maria Thun on the fields at Dexbach

soils that Maria worked with were generally good. In order to demonstrate that her results were not dependent on soil quality, she set out to find a farm with poor light soils, which she found in Dexbach, Hessen – an area of grassland on shale soil. The Thuns bought a small farm there and moved in 1975. It was more difficult to cultivate this piece of grassland than had originally been thought since, when ploughing, one immediately struck the stony shale. Only gradually with the help of the barrel preparation (manure concentrate or cow pat preparation) did the ground become something that could be described as an arable field.

Around this time Maria Thun began her first 'peppering' trials. The work with weed peppers proved to be unexpectedly diverse. It took a while before Maria managed to 'cultivate' weeds herself, collect the seeds, find the right way of producing the ash and, after several years, discover the best time to burn the seeds.

In 2003 she began work on the tree bark preparations. They were her last major subjects of study and were close to her heart.

In 2007, at the age of 85, Maria began to pass responsibility on to her children. Since 1972, Christina and Matthias had been fully engaged with the practical aspects of the research and with publishing the results.

Throughout her life Maria Thun continued to bring up new questions and did whatevever was in her power to find answers. She did so with great strength and willpower, was never satisfied with half measures and was not discouraged when things didn't work out. This strength and inner searching was hers to the very end. It was not easy for her to pass her work on to her successors and she continued to take part as long as she could in all aspects of the work.

The barrel preparation
(manure concentrate or cow pat preparation)
Titia Thun and Friedrich Thun

The barrel preparation, developed by Maria Thun, is an extension of the standard compost preparations used in biodynamic agriculture. She developed it in the late 1950s and early 1960s in response to high levels of radioactive strontium-90. For a brief period she worked together with Ehrenfried Pfeiffer, developing ideas and research projects before he died in 1961. Their starting point was the research results of an institute that indicated that the deposition of strontium-90 varied in different areas – limestone having far fewer deposits than granite.

Maria Thun took up these ideas and began trials with different kinds of limestone. She had great difficulty in finding someone who could assess the radiation during the process. In the 1960s the atomic industry dominated radiation research, which was therefore reserved for institutions that were supportive of nuclear power. Those who agreed to help evaluate her research insisted that the results should not be published for fear that the information might be misused to make their life difficult.

By the time the barrel preparation had been fully developed in the 1970s the threat posed by strontium-90 had all but disappeared. The preparation, however, had many beneficial attributes and brought about an excellent transformation and vitalisation of the soil. It was shown to enhance decomposition and humus formation, and soil treated with it had a better, deeper structure. For these reasons it has been found to be an effective preparation for farms in conversion to biodynamics.

Apart from counteracting strontium-90 pollution, the barrel preparation was found to be helpful in other situations. In regions affected by the airborn radioactivity from the Chernobyl disaster, three applications of the preparation resulted in radiation being reduced by around 60%. On farms where the preparation had been used for a long time there was evidence of little or no radioactive presence in the plants despite neighbouring farms being strongly affected. Unfortunately none of the research institutes that had recorded positive results in terms of reduced radioactivity were prepared to provide written confirmation of the results. Therefore, the status of this important effect of the barrel preparation remains 'not yet scientifically proven'. This became a problem once again with the Fukushima disaster, when the search for solutions could only include what has been scientifically proven.

Production of the barrel preparation

Materials:

- 5 10-litre (2½ gal) buckets of cow manure
- 100 g (3½ oz) crushed eggshells
- 500 g (1 lb) basalt meal/sand
- 2 wooden barrels (one to dynamise the material, one to put into the ground) about 70 cm (27 in) high, 40 cm (16 in) in diameter
- the six compost preparations

The preparation that was developed used the above quantity ratios and materials. Experimentation has shown other proportions to be less favourable and to have a reduced effect.

For the basic material, five round buckets of well-formed, firm cow manure are required. The manure should be from a biodynamic farm and from female, horned animals that have calved at least once. They should be fed roughage such as hay or straw until they produce firm, well-formed cow pats. Since this fodder is likely to reduce milk production the manure should be taken from dry cows.

Eggshells should be from free-range hens. They can be from boiled or fresh eggs from the kitchen, and the skin should remain on the egg. Crumble them to the consistency of meal or sand but not as fine as flour. A coffee grinder (set for coarse grinding) can be used, but the material should not heat up in the process.

The basalt meal should consist of grains of 1 mm – sandy, but not like flour. Basalt can easily be bought from stone merchants or online. Ground rock should not be used as it usually contains granite or other rocks.

For a container, use a wooden barrel cut in half or a similar wooden container. We advise against using plastic or cemented brick containers.

Put the manure, egg shells and basalt in the container. Move the contents in a circular motion around the barrel with a spade for exactly one hour. It is also important to do this for the whole hour, and also to do the mixing by hand, not using a stirring machine. The aim is to consider these substances as contributing to the formation of a kind of organism. In bringing about an organism the use of machines should be avoided as far as possible.

After the material has been dynamised for an hour, the second barrel is needed. Remove its base and bury it to half its depth in the ground. Heap the earth that is dug out around the barrel so that it is completely surrounded with soil. If the soil is not deep enough, it can be raised by surrounding the barrel with soil from elsewhere.

The cow dung ready for the dynamising process to begin

Place half of the dynamised manure in the barrel and insert the five compost preparations (not valerian), always with the stinging nettle in the centre. The jars containing the preparations can be positioned around the barrel to mark where they were inserted. The second half of the dynamised manure is then added and the preparations are inserted a second time. Always place the same preparation above in the same position. Once inserted, cover the preparations with some manure.

Finally, put 1 litre (quart) of water into a 2-litre glass or pottery container and add 10 drops of valerian preparation. Stir this for about 10 minutes. Then sprinkle this evenly over the manure in the barrel. As a reminder, pin the production date (and lunar constellation) to the rim of the barrel, and close with a wooden cover. After four weeks mix the

The compost preparations are inserted in the dynamised manure. Place the jars around the barrel to mark the positions before adding the second layer.

contents of the barrel with a spade, and after a further four weeks it is ready to use.

To have good quality barrel preparation two things should be considered. The barrel in the ground should not be located on energy or ley lines, which can be found using a divining rod. It is also important to use the correct cosmic constellation. When it is deposited, the cow manure absorbs the influence of the constellation of that particular moment. The time for turning and preparing it in the barrel is also important. The best time for this work is when the Moon is in Leo or Virgo.

The time of year also needs careful consideration and must be frost free. The time span from spring to the end of summer is recommended since the preparation needs warmth for its maturation. In frost-free regions the preparation can be produced throughout the year. The times shown as unfavourable in the calendar should be avoided. Manure that has been collected or that has been dynamised should not be left out in the rain as this will not result in a good preparation.

The finished preparation must then be stirred again, but this time only for 20 minutes. The preparation should if possible be stirred in wooden, earthenware or glass cylindrical containers. We have obtained the best results from containers with a height to diameter ratio of 2:3.

With horn manure we use 30 g for 10 litres of stirred liquid (1 oz for 2½ gal). In the case of barrel preparation we use twice that, 60 g (2 oz for 2½ gal). The 10 litres that have been stirred is enough for an area of about ¼ ha (2½ gal for ½ acre) sprayed with a knapsack sprayer. The water used should be left to stand for a whole day so that it can adapt to the surrounding temperature and absorb the light.

The effectiveness of the stirred barrel preparation lasts for four days. During this time it should be sprayed three times directly on the soil at dusk or when the soil is cultivated. This will optimise the effect.

Because the barrel preparation strongly stimulates the transformation process, it is important not to use it exclusively but to also spray horn manure preparation before or after sowing. Otherwise the rotting process in the soil may also affect the plants, and cause their roots to decay.

The tree bark preparations
Titia Thun and Friedrich Thun

Compost preparations have been used by biodynamic farmers for many years in order to improve soil fermentation and enhance the processes of life. The indications given by Rudolf Steiner for these preparations involve using animal organs such as stag bladders as well as bovine intestines, mesenteries and the skull of a domestic animal. With the strict regulations imposed in response to BSE, access to these animal parts became more difficult and so in 2003 Maria Thun began to develop what she called tree bark preparations.

She sought to replace the animal organ ingredients (apart from manure) and settled on sheaths formed by the bark of trees. In doing so, she departed from the preparations as Rudolf Steiner had described them, which is why these tree bark preparations are not counted among the biodynamic preparations. They are nonetheless based on bio-dynamic principles, and in developing them Maria Thun made a deep study of the fundamentals of anthroposophy. The preparations she developed aim to support the work of biodynamic farmers by offering an alternative where the animal sheaths are unobtainable because of BSE regulations or other reasons.

The compost preparations, whether made with plant or animal sheaths, are linked to and influenced by specific planets. Animal organs simplify this process, which is why they are easier to apply. To achieve a similar objective with plant-based materials requires greater precision. The type of tree chosen for these plant sheaths is connected with the relevant planet and during the production process particular planetary aspects must be found to support it. It is therefore important to follow the guidelines exactly. Any departure from the recommended times can have a strong influence on how effective the preparations are. We give all the possible times, so that a suitable one can be found. Since the necessary aspects do not recur in a regular rhythm, it can happen that in some years the appropriate aspect does not occur. Because of this we always recommend making sufficient preparation to last more than one year, so that it can, if necessary, bridge the gap. The amount of material

One yarrow preparation in an animal sheath (stag bladder) and two in a plant-based sheath (birch bark). Hanging in a sunny, dry position over the summer (left), and ready to be buried over winter (right).

made should also be increased since about a third more preparation is needed than when animal sheaths are used.

Maria Thun began to work with these plant-based preparations in the last years of her life, and though she came to a clear result, the work on these preparations is far from finished. We plan to continue with this work.

Producing the plant-based preparations

To make the plant-based preparations a branch of the appropriate tree is cut and the wood in the centre is removed so that as far as possible only the bark remains. Some plant-based fibres can be used to hold the bark together. This container of bark is then filled and treated in the same way as the biodynamic preparations.

Yarrow (equivalent to 502)

This preparation is linked to the planet Venus; the wood we use as a sheath is therefore taken from the birch. The preparation is treated like the stag bladder, hung up over the summer in a dry sunny place, buried the following winter 30–50 cm (12–20 in) deep in the earth, and then dug out in spring two or three weeks after the earth has warmed up.

Left: the bark sheaths are filled   *Right: ready to be buried in the soil*

Camomile (equivalent to 503)

This preparation is linked to the planet Mercury; the wood used comes from the larch. It is treated in the same way as with the bovine intestine, buried 30–50 cm (12–20 in) deep in the earth and dug out in spring two or three weeks after the soil has warmed up.

Oak (equivalent to 504)

The oak is linked to Mars and as may be expected also provides the sheath. The preparation is treated in the same way as the skull. It is placed into moist soil with a constant gentle flow of water and in spring it is taken out two or three weeks after the soil has warmed up.

Dandelion (equivalent to 506)

This preparation is connected to Jupiter; the wood used for a sheath is from the maple. It is treated in the same way as the bovine mesentery. It is buried in the earth about 50 cm (20 in) deep and taken out in spring two or three weeks after the earth has warmed up.

The *stinging nettle preparation (504)* and the *valerian preparation (507)* need no animal sheath and so no plant-based alternative is required.

Further reading

Berrevoets, Erik, *Wisdom of Bees: Principles of Biodynamic Beekeeping*, SteinerBooks, USA

Colquhoun, Margaret and Axel Ewald, *New Eyes for Plants*, Hawthorn

Florin, Jean-Michel (ed.) *Biodynamic Wine Growing: Understanding the Vine and Its Rhythms*, Floris

Karlsson, Britt and Per, *Biodynamic, Organic and Natural Winemaking*, Floris

Keyserlink, Adalbert Count von, *The Birth of a New Agriculture*, Temple Lodge

—, *Developing Biodynamic Agriculture*, Temple Lodge

Klett, Manfred, *The Foundations and Principles of Biodynamic Preparations*, Floris

Klocek, Dennis, *Sacred Agriculture: The Alchemy of Biodynamics*, Lindisfarne

Koepf, H.H., *The Biodynamic Farm: Agriculture in the Service of Humanity*, SteinerBooks, USA

—, *Koepf's Practical Biodynamics: Soil, Compost, Sprays and Food Quality*, Floris

König, Karl, *Social Farming: Healing Humanity and the Earth*, Floris

Kranich, Ernst Michael, *Planetary Influences upon Plants*, Biodynamic Association, USA

Masson, Pierre, *A Biodynamic Manual*, Floris

Morrow, Joel, *Vegetable Gardening for Organic and Biodynamic Growers*, Lindisfarne

Osthaus, K.-E., *The Biodynamic Farm*, Floris

Pfeiffer, Ehrenfried, *Pfeiffer's Introduction to Biodynamics*, Floris

—, *Weeds and What They Tell Us*, Floris

—, & Michael Maltas, *The Biodynamic Orchard Book*, Floris

Philbrick, John and Helen, *Gardening for Health and Nutrition*, Anthroposophic, USA

Philbrick, Helen & Gregg, Richard B., *Companion Plants: An A to Z for Gardeners and Farmers*, Floris

Sattler, Friedrich & Eckard von Wistinghausen, *Growing Biodynamic Crops*, Floris

Selg, Peter, *The Agricultural Course: Rudolf Steiner and the Beginnings of Biodynamics*, Temple Lodge

Steiner, Rudolf, *Agriculture (A Course of Eight Lectures)*, Biodynamic Association, USA (also published in another translation by Rudolf Steineer Press, UK)

—, *Agriculture: An Introductory Reader*, Steiner Press, UK

—, *What is Biodynamics? A Way to Heal and Revitalize the Earth*, SteinerBooks, USA

Storl, Wolf, *Culture and Horticulture*, North Atlantic Books, USA

Thun, Maria, *Gardening for Life*, Hawthorn

—, *The Biodynamic Year*, Temple Lodge

Thun, Matthias, *Biodynamic Beekeeping*, Floris

Weiler, Michael, *The Secret of Bees: An Insider's Guide to the Life of the Honeybee*, Floris

Wright, Hilary, *Biodynamic Gardening for Health and Taste*, Floris

Biodynamic associations

Demeter International
    www.demeter.net
Australia:
    Australian Demeter Bio-Dynamic
    demeterbiodynamic.com.au/
    Biodynamic Agriculture Australia
    www.biodynamics.net.au
Canada (Ontario): Society for Bio-Dynamic Farming & Gardening in Ontario
    biodynamics.on.ca (see also USA)
India: Bio-Dynamic Association of India (BDAI)
    www.biodynamics.in

Ireland: Biodynamic Agriculture Association of Ireland
    www.biodynamicagriculture.ie
New Zealand:
    NZ Biodynamic Association
    www.biodynamic.org.nz
South Africa: Biodynamic Agricultural Association of Southern Africa
    www.bdaasa.org.za
UK: Biodynamic Association
    www.biodynamic.org.uk
USA: Biodynamic Assoc. of North America
    www.biodynamics.com